HSE

Health and Safety
Executive

Control of substances hazardous to health

The Control of Substances Hazardous to Health Regulations
2002 (as amended)

Approved Code of Practice and guidance

GW00671205

London: TSO

Published by TSO (The Stationery Office), part of Williams Lea,
and available from:

Online
https://books.hse.gov.uk/

Mail, Telephone, Fax & E-mail
TSO
PO Box 29, Norwich, NR3 1GN
Telephone orders/General enquiries: 0333 202 5070
Fax orders: 0333 202 5080
E-mail: customer.services@tso.co.uk
Textphone 0333 202 5077

TSO@Blackwell and other Accredited Agents

© Crown copyright 2013

First published 1995
Sixth edition 2013

ISBN 978 0 7176 6582 2

This information is licensed under the Open Government Licence v3.0. To view this licence,
visit http://www.nationalarchives.gov.uk/doc/open-government-licence/ **OGL**

Any enquiries regarding this publication should be sent to: copyright@hse.gov.uk

Some images and illustrations in this publication may not be owned by the Crown and cannot be reproduced
without permission of the copyright owner. Where we have identified any third party copyright information
you will need to obtain permission from the copyright holders concerned. Enquiries should be sent to
copyright@hse.gov.uk

Printed in the United Kingdom for The Stationery Office.
J003661516 c1 04/20

Approved Code of Practice

This Code has been approved by the Health and Safety Executive, with the consent of the Secretary of State.
It gives practical advice on how to comply with the law. If you follow the advice you will be doing enough to
comply with the law in respect of those specific matters on which the Code gives advice. You may use
alternative methods to those set out in the Code in order to comply with the law.

However, the Code has a special legal status. If you are prosecuted for breach of health and safety law, and
it is proved that you did not follow the relevant provisions of the Code, you will need to show that you have
complied with the law in some other way or a Court will find you at fault.

Guidance

This guidance is issued by the Health and Safety Executive. Following the guidance is not compulsory,
unless specifically stated, and you are free to take other action. But if you do follow the guidance you will
normally be doing enough to comply with the law. Health and safety inspectors seek to secure compliance
with the law and may refer to this guidance.

Contents

Introduction

1   This publication contains the Approved Code of Practice (ACOP) for the Control of Substances Hazardous to Health (COSHH) Regulations 2002 as amended by the:

■   Control of Substances Hazardous to Health (Amendment) Regulations 2003 (SI 2003/978)
■   Carriage of Dangerous Goods and Use of Transportable Pressure Equipment Regulations 2004 (SI 2004/568)
■   Control of Substances Hazardous to Health (Amendment) Regulations 2004 (SI 2004/3386)
■   Health and Safety (Enforcing Authority for Railways and Other Guided Transport Systems) Regulations 2006 (SI 2006/557)
■   Carriage of Dangerous Goods and Use of Transportable Pressure Equipment Regulations 2007 (SI 2007/1573)
■   Coal Dust (Control of Inhalable Dust) Regulations 2007 (SI 2007/1894)
■   Legislative Reform (Health and Safety Executive) Order 2008 (SI 2008/960)
■   Registration, Evaluation, Authorisation and restriction of CHemicals (REACH) Enforcement Regulations 2008 (SI 2008/2852)
■   Chemicals (Hazard Information and Packaging for Supply) Regulations 2009 (SI 2009/716)
■   Control of Asbestos Regulations 2012 (SI 2012/632)

2   The ACOP covers all substances to which the COSHH Regulations 2002 as amended apply.

3   This publication is aimed at dutyholders and health and safety professionals, but managers and health and safety representatives may also find it useful.

4   Material supporting regulations 7, 9, 10 and 11 has been updated to take account of regulatory changes, such as the introduction of the EU Regulations for REACH and Classification, Labelling and Packaging (CLP), and to clarify the requirements of the Regulations.

About ACOPs

5   Approved Codes of Practice are approved by the HSE Board with the consent of the Secretary of State (see Appendix 1: Notice of Approval for details).

6   The ACOP describes the preferred or recommended methods that can be used (or the standards to be met) to comply with the Regulations and the duties imposed by the Health and Safety at Work etc Act 1974 (HSW Act). The accompanying guidance also provides advice on achieving compliance, or it may give information of a general nature, including explanation of the requirements of the law, more specific technical information or references to further sources of information.

7   The legal status of ACOP and guidance text is given on page 2.

Presentation

8   In this publication, the ACOP text is set out in **bold** and the accompanying guidance in normal type, the text of the Regulations is in *italics*. Coloured borders also indicate each section clearly.

The Regulations

Regulation 1 Citation and commencement

Regulation	1

These Regulations may be cited as the Control of Substances Hazardous to Health Regulations 2002 and shall come into force on 21st November 2002.

Regulation 2 Interpretation

Regulation	2

(1)   In these Regulations –

"the 1974 Act" means the Health and Safety at Work etc Act 1974;

"the Agreement" means the Agreement on the European Economic Area signed at Oporto on 2nd May 1992 as adjusted by the Protocol signed at Brussels on 17th March 1993 and adopted as respects Great Britain by the European Economic Area Act 1993;

"appointed doctor" means a registered medical practitioner appointed for the time being in writing by the Executive for the purpose of these Regulations;

"approved" means approved for the time being in writing;

"approved classification" of a biological agent means the classification of that agent approved by the Health and Safety Executive;[a]

"biological agent" means a micro-organism, cell culture, or human endoparasite, whether or not genetically modified, which may cause infection, allergy, toxicity or otherwise create a hazard to human health;

"carcinogen" means –

(a)   a substance or preparation which if classified in accordance with the classification provided for by regulation 4 of the CHIP Regulations would be in the category of danger, carcinogenic (category 1) or carcinogenic (category 2) whether or not the substance or preparation would be required to be classified under those Regulations; or

(b)   a substance or preparation –
(i)   listed in Schedule 1; or
(ii)   arising from a process specified in Schedule 1 which is a substance hazardous to health;

"cell culture" means the in-vitro growth of cells derived from multicellular organisms;

"the CHIP Regulations" means the Chemicals (Hazard Information and Packaging for Supply) Regulations 2009;[b]

Regulation   **2**

"The CLP Regulation" means Regulation (EC) No 1272/2008 of the European Parliament and of the Council on classification, labelling and packaging of substances and mixtures amending and repealing Directives 67/548/EEC and 1999/45/EC, and amending Regulation (EC) No 1907/2006;[b]

"control measure" means a measure taken to reduce exposure to a substance hazardous to health (including the provision of systems of work and supervision, the cleaning of workplaces, premises, plant and equipment, the provision and use of engineering controls and personal protective equipment);

"employment medical adviser" means an employment medical adviser appointed under section 56 of the Health and Safety at Work etc Act 1974;

"the Executive" means the Health and Safety Executive;

"fumigation" means an operation in which a substance is released into the atmosphere so as to form a gas to control or kill pests or other undesirable organisms and "fumigate" and "fumigant" shall be construed accordingly;

"Group", in relation to a biological agent, means one of the four hazard Groups specified in paragraph 2 of Schedule 3 to which that agent is assigned;

"hazard", in relation to a substance, means the intrinsic property of that substance which has the potential to cause harm to the health of a person, and "hazardous" shall be construed accordingly;

"health surveillance" means assessment of the state of health of an employee, as related to exposure to substances hazardous to health, and includes biological monitoring;

"inhalable dust" means airborne material which is capable of entering the nose and mouth during breathing, as defined by BS EN 481 1993;

"medical examination" includes any laboratory tests and X-rays that a relevant doctor may require;

"member State" means a State which is a Contracting Party to the Agreement;

"micro-organism" means a microbiological entity, cellular or non-cellular, which is capable of replication or of transferring genetic material;

"mine" has the meaning assigned to it by section 180 of the Mines and Quarries Act 1954;

"mutagen" means a substance or preparation which if classified in accordance with the classification provided for by regulation 4 of the Chemicals (Hazard Information and Packaging for Supply) Regulations 2002 would be in the category of danger, mutagenic (category 1) or mutagenic (category 2) whether or not the substance or preparation would be required to be classified under those Regulations;

"personal protective equipment" means all equipment (including clothing) which is intended to be worn or held by a person at work and which protects that person against one or more risks to his health, and any addition or accessory designed to meet that objective;

"preparation" means a mixture or solution of two or more substances;

Regulation   2

"public road" means (in England and Wales) a highway maintainable at the public expense within the meaning of section 329 of the Highways Act 1980 and (in Scotland) a public road within the meaning assigned to that term by section 151 of the Roads (Scotland) Act 1984;

"registered dentist" has the meaning assigned to it in section 53(1) of the Dentists Act 1984;

"relevant doctor" means an appointed doctor or an employment medical adviser;

"respirable dust" means airborne material which is capable of penetrating to the gas exchange region of the lung, as defined by BS EN 481 1993;

"risk", in relation to the exposure of an employee to a substance hazardous to health, means the likelihood that the potential for harm to the health of a person will be attained under the conditions of use and exposure and also the extent of that harm;

"the risk assessment" means the assessment of risk required by regulation 6(1)(a);

"risk phrase" has the meaning assigned to it in regulation 2(1) of the CHIP Regulations;

"safety data sheet" means a safety data sheet within the meaning of Regulation (EC) No 1907/2006 of the European Parliament and of the Council concerning the Registration, Evaluation, Authorisation and Restriction of Chemicals;[b]

"substance" means a natural or artificial substance whether in solid or liquid form or in the form of a gas or vapour (including micro-organisms);

"substance hazardous to health" means a substance (including a preparation) –

(a) *which is listed in Table 3.2 of part 3 of Annex VI of the CLP Regulation[b] and for which an indication of danger specified for the substance is very toxic, toxic, harmful, corrosive or irritant;*
(b) *for which the Health and Safety Executive[a] has approved a workplace exposure limit;*
(c) *which is a biological agent;*
(d) *which is dust of any kind, except dust which is a substance within paragraph (a) or (b) above, when present at a concentration in air equal to or greater than –*
  (i) *10 mg/m³, as a time-weighted average over an 8-hour period, of inhalable dust; or*
  (ii) *4 mg/m³, as a time-weighted average over an 8-hour period, of respirable dust;*
(e) *which, not being a substance falling within sub-paragraphs (a) to (d), because of its chemical or toxicological properties and the way it is used or is present at the workplace creates a risk to health;*

"workplace" means any premises or part of premises used for or in connection with work, and includes –

(a) *any place within the premises to which an employee has access while at work; and*
(b) *any room, lobby, corridor, staircase, road or other place –*
  (i) *used as a means of access to or egress from that place of work; or*

Regulation 2

(ii) where facilities are provided for use in connection with that place of work,
other than a public road.

"workplace exposure limit" for a substance hazardous to health means the exposure limit approved by the Health and Safety Executive for that substance in relation to the specified reference period when calculated by a method approved by the Health and Safety Executive, as contained in HSE publication "EH40 Workplace Exposure Limits 2005" as updated from time to time.

(2) In these Regulations, a reference to an employee being exposed to a substance hazardous to health is a reference to the exposure of that employee to a substance hazardous to health arising out of or in connection with work at the workplace.

(3) Where a biological agent has an approved classification, any reference in these Regulations to a particular Group in relation to that agent shall be taken as a reference to the Group to which that agent has been assigned in that approved classification.

(a) Transitional provisions specified by Legislative Reform (Health and Safety Executive) Order 2008/960.
(b) Modified by the Chemicals (Hazard Information and Packaging for Supply) Regulations 2009/716.

Guidance 2

Substances hazardous to health

9   COSHH applies to a wide range of substances and preparations (mixtures of two or more substances) which have the potential to cause harm to health if they are ingested, inhaled, or are absorbed by, or come into contact with, the skin, or other body membranes. Hazardous substances can occur in many forms, including solids, liquids, vapours, gases and fumes. They can also be simple asphyxiants or biological agents (see paragraphs 14–23).

10   Employers should regard a substance as hazardous to health if it is hazardous in the form in which it may occur in the work activity. A substance hazardous to health need not be just a chemical compound, it can also include mixtures of compounds, micro-organisms or natural materials, such as flour, stone or wood dust.

11   Regulation 2(1) includes a number of specific definitions of a 'substance hazardous to health' for the purpose of these Regulations. However, sub-paragraph 2(1)(e) brings within the scope of the Regulations any substance not covered by the specific descriptions in sub-paragraphs (a)–(d) but, due to its chemical or toxicological properties and the way it is used or present at the workplace, creates a risk to health, for example animal fur, or dander, which can cause occupational asthma.

12   Dust of any kind can also become a substance hazardous to health under COSHH when it is present at concentrations in the air equal to or greater than 10 mg/m^3 (as a time-weighted average over an eight-hour period) of inhalable dust or 4 mg/m^3 (as a time-weighted average over an eight-hour period) of respirable dust. However, there may be dusts with no formal workplace exposure limit (WEL) which are not listed in CLP, but for which limits lower than 10 mg/m^3 or 4 mg/m^3 would be appropriate because of evidence of potential hazards to health. For these dusts, employers are advised to set their own in-house standards.

13   The definitions of 'inhalable dust' and 'respirable dust' include references to BS EN 481:1993 *Workplace atmospheres. Size fraction definitions for measurement of airborne particles*.[1] This is the English language version of the European Standard approved by the European Committee for Standardization (CEN).

14   COSHH covers those gases and vapours which, when present at high concentrations in air at the workplace, act as simple asphyxiants. These can displace the oxygen content to such an extent that life cannot be supported. Many of these asphyxiant gases are odourless, colourless and not readily detectable. Monitoring the oxygen content of the air is a means of assessing whether their presence poses a risk to the health of employees.

15   For some gases and vapours, eg flammable gases and vapours or poisonous or asphyxiant gases, there may be other risks associated with their use and presence in the air, eg fire and explosion, sudden collapse or asphyxiation. There may be additional duties in respect of flammable asphyxiant gases that satisfy the definition of 'dangerous substance' as set out in the Dangerous Substances and Explosive Atmospheres Regulations 2002 (DSEAR) and/or for those used in an enclosed environment in respect of the Confined Spaces Regulations 1997.

Biological agents

16   Biological agents may also be considered to be substances hazardous to health and include:

- micro-organisms such as bacteria, viruses, fungi, and the agents that cause transmissible spongiform encephalopathies (TSEs);
- cell cultures, if the cell being cultured is itself hazardous;
- parasites that live inside their host, including single-cell organisms, eg malarial parasites, amoebae and trypanosomes and the microscopic infectious forms of larger parasites, eg the microscopic ova and infectious larval (helminths).

17   External larger parasites, such as ticks and mosquitoes, are not biological agents, but their bite may be the route by which a parasite or pathogen can infect a human.

18   The general duties of COSHH apply to incidental exposure to, and deliberate work with, biological agents. However, COSHH does not cover a situation where, for example, one employee catches a respiratory infection from another. This is because regulation 2(2) specifies that COSHH only applies in those circumstances where risks of exposure are work related, and not those where they have no direct connection with the work being done.

19   Incidental exposure to biological agents can occur when an employee's work activity brings them into contact with material which contains infectious agents, eg blood, body fluids, contaminated water, waste material or bedding/laundry etc. Where there is a risk from exposure to legionella bacteria, specific information is available in *Legionnaires' disease: The control of legionella bacteria in water systems*.[2]

20   Exposure can also occur as a result of deliberate planned work with a biological agent in microbiological containment facilities ('contained use' facilities), eg research, development, teaching or diagnosis, and in production facilities (pharmaceutical or veterinary medicine).

Guidance 2

21   Biological agents are classified into four 'hazard groups' according to the following infection criteria:

■   their ability to cause infection;
■   the severity of the disease that may result;
■   the risk that infection will spread to the community;
■   the availability of vaccines and effective treatment.

22   The four hazard groups of biological agents and their descriptions are set out in paragraph 2(2) of Schedule 3 to these Regulations. Biological agents in Hazard Groups 2–4 are given an approved classification in *The Approved List of biological agents*[3] according to the above infection criteria. Where a biological agent is also toxic or allergenic this is indicated in the list. Some biological agents are not infectious (so fall into Hazard Group 1 and are not listed) but may still be toxic or allergenic.

23   If the work involves genetic modification of a biological agent, the employer will also need to consider the Genetically Modified Organisms (Contained Use) Regulations 2000 (www.hse.gov.uk/biosafety/gmo/).

Carcinogens and mutagens

24   Regulation 7(5) of COSHH includes special provisions for preventing or adequately controlling exposure to carcinogens and mutagens. Scientific research continues to find further substances and processes which are suspected, with varying degrees of confidence, of causing cancer or of causing heritable genetic damage. It is important, therefore, for employers to have an active precautionary policy of prevention and control. This should be based on up-to-date knowledge of the substances which are suspected of being carcinogenic or mutagenic, but which are not yet subject to the special provisions for carcinogens and mutagens contained in regulation 7.

25   Particular caution is needed with substances which have not previously been considered to be hazardous in this way, or perhaps in any way, as they are more likely to have been used without particular care. With all diseases, prevention is better than cure. Where the effects of exposure can be irreversible, prevention may be the only option.

26   Under CHIP, the descriptors assigned to the three categories of carcinogens are:

■   Carcinogenic Category 1 – substances known to cause cancer on the basis of human experience;
■   Carcinogenic Category 2 – substances which it is assumed can cause cancer on the basis of reliable animal evidence;
■   Carcinogenic Category 3 – substances where there is only evidence in animals and it is of doubtful relevance to human health (ie the evidence is not good enough for Categories 1 or 2).

27   In the case of mutagens, there are three similar categories with analogous descriptors, based on the strength of evidence for heritable genetic damage.

28   Category 3 carcinogens are not included in the COSHH definitions of 'carcinogen' and 'mutagen', respectively, but are subject to the general requirements of COSHH. A comprehensive list of substances defined as carcinogens or mutagens for the purposes of COSHH is in EH40/2005 *Workplace exposure limits*.[4] (Also see paragraph 33.)

Asthmagens

29   Asthma is characterised by periodic attacks of wheezing, chest tightness or breathlessness resulting from constriction of the airways. A substance is considered to cause occupational asthma if, as a result of exposures in the workplace, it both:

■   produces the biological change known as the hypersensitive state in the airways; and
■   triggers a subsequent reaction in those airways.

30   'Cause' does not, in this context, mean triggering an asthmatic attack in a person who has asthma due to another, unrelated cause (occupational or non-occupational). Occupational asthma may be caused by manufactured chemicals or naturally occurring materials, such as fungal spores.

Other points to consider

31   Regulation 2(1) includes a definition of 'The CLP Regulation'. This is a European Regulation on Classification, Labelling and Packaging of Substances and Mixtures. It entered into legal effect in all EU member states on 20 January 2009, subject to a lengthy transitional period. Its provisions will be phased in until 1 June 2015, when the CLP Regulation will be fully in force.

32   The existing framework of risk and safety phrases will be replaced, and new harmonised warning and precautionary statements for labels will be introduced. The risk phrases R42, R42/43, R45, R46 and R49 listed in regulation 7(7) will gradually be replaced with the following hazard statements:

■   H350 – may cause cancer;
■   H340 – may cause genetic defects;
■   H350i – may cause cancer by inhalation;
■   H334 – may cause allergy or asthma symptoms or breathing difficulties if inhaled;
■   H317 – may cause an allergic skin reaction.

33   In addition, CLP (Table 3.6.1 of Annex I) classifies carcinogens into two categories, the first of which may be divided again into sub-categories:

■   Category 1 – known or presumed to have carcinogenic potential for humans:
    – Category 1A: an assessment based primarily on human evidence;
    – Category 1B: an assessment based primarily on animal evidence;
■   Category 2 – suspected human carcinogens.

34   Further information can be found on the European Chemicals Agency (ECHA) website at http://echa.europa.eu/web/guest/regulations/clp.

35   When deciding whether the substances used or produced in the workplace are covered by COSHH, employers should also consider the following:

■   Different forms of a substance may present different hazards, eg substances may not be hazardous in solid form but may be hazardous when ground into fine powder or dust that can be breathed into the lungs.
■   Nanoparticles (ie particles less than 100 nanometers) may be more toxic than larger particles of the same chemical substance.
■   Impurities in a substance can make it more hazardous, eg crystalline silica is often present in minerals which would otherwise present little or no hazard.

Guidance   2

- Some substances have a fibrous form which may present a potentially serious risk to health if the fibres are of a certain size or shape.
- Some substances have a known health effect but the mechanism causing it is unknown, eg certain dusts of textile raw materials cause byssinosis.
- Exposure to two or more substances at the same time or one after the other may have an added or synergistic effect.
- Epidemiological or other data, eg reports of illness due to new and emerging agents, indicate that a biological agent that does not already appear in *The Approved List of biological agents* could nevertheless cause a hazard to health.
- One-off, emergency situations arising out of the work activity, such as a dangerous chemical reaction or fire, could foreseeably produce a substance hazardous to health.
- 'Wet work' is one of the most frequently and consistently reported causes of irritant occupational contact dermatitis. 'Wet work' is the term used to describe tasks involving prolonged or frequent contact with water, particularly in combination with soaps and detergents.

The workplace

36   The definition of 'workplace' in COSHH is based on that used in the Workplace (Health, Safety and Welfare) Regulations 1992[5] but is wider in scope as it also applies to domestic premises, ie private dwellings. Certain words in the definition are themselves defined in section 53 of the HSW Act.[6]

37   'Premises' means any place (whether or not there is a structure at that place). It includes vehicles, vessels, any land-based or offshore installations, movable areas to which employees have access while at work, and their means of access to and exit from the workplace. Common parts of shared buildings, private roads and paths on industrial estates and business parks are included.

38   Public roads which are used to get to or from the workplace are not covered by the definition. However, in some circumstances a public road may itself become the workplace, and if substances hazardous to health are used or produced during the work activity, COSHH may apply, eg road repairing or resurfacing, kerbstone cutting, line painting etc.

Regulation 3 Duties under these Regulations

Regulation   3

(1)   Where a duty is placed by these Regulations on an employer in respect of his employees, he shall, so far as is reasonably practicable, be under a like duty in respect of any other person, whether at work or not, who may be affected by the work carried out by the employer except that the duties of the employer –

(a)   under regulation 11 (health surveillance) shall not extend to persons who are not his employees; and

(b)   under regulations 10, 12(1) and (2) and 13 (which relate respectively to monitoring, information and training and dealing with accidents) shall not extend to persons who are not his employees, unless those persons are on the premises where the work is being carried out.

(2)   These Regulations shall apply to a self-employed person as they apply to an employer and an employee and as if that self-employed person were both an employer and an employee, except that regulations 10 and 11 shall not apply to a self-employed person.

(3)   These Regulations shall not apply to the master or crew of a ship or to the employer of such persons in respect of the normal shipboard activities of a ship's crew which –

(a)   are carried out solely by the crew under the direction of the master; and
(b)   are not liable to expose persons other than the master and crew to a risk to their health and safety,

and for the purposes of this paragraph "ship" includes every description of vessel used in navigation, other than a ship forming part of Her Majesty's Navy.

Duties of employers

39   Table 1 summarises the scope of the employer's duties under COSHH towards employees and other people likely to be affected by the work, eg contractors, visitors to a site and, where biological agents are concerned, patients in a hospital or visitors to a petting zoo. However, there may be more wide-ranging requirements, eg under the Management of Health and Safety at Work (MHSW) Regulations. SFARP stands for 'so far as reasonably practicable' and an explanation of this is provided at www.hse.gov.uk/risk/faq/htm.

Table 1 The employer's duties

Duty of employer relating to:	Duty for the protection of:		
	Employees	**Other people on the premises**	**Other people likely to be affected by the work**
Assessment (regulation 6)	Yes	SFARP	SFARP
Prevention/control of exposure (regulation 7)	Yes	SFARP	SFARP
Use of control measures and maintenance, examination and test of control measures (regulations 8 and 9)	Yes	SFARP	SFARP
Monitoring exposure (regulation 10)	Yes, where required	SFARP	No
Health surveillance (regulation 11)	Yes, where appropriate	No	No
Information, training etc (regulation 12)	Yes	SFARP	No
Arrangements to deal with accidents and emergencies (regulation 13)	Yes	SFARP	No

The visiting employer

40   When working at another employer's premises, the two employers should co-operate and collaborate to ensure that all the duties imposed by COSHH are fulfilled. They may need to decide which of them will carry out a particular duty. For example, it is usually appropriate for the employer who creates the risk to carry out

any necessary monitoring of exposure. On larger sites, it is sometimes the practice for the contractor in overall charge to arrange for health surveillance to be provided for all those working on the site exposed to hazardous substances, including employees of subcontractors; regulation 2(2) is not intended to discourage this.

The employer occupying the premises

41   The employer occupying the premises should provide the visiting employer with sufficient information about any substances hazardous to health that may be used or produced at the premises. This information should be detailed enough to allow the visiting employer to provide their own employees with information and instruction on complying with the occupying employer's control measures.

42   The occupier of the premises will also need to know about any substances hazardous to health that are likely to be used or produced by the work the visiting employer will be doing. This information is essential so that the occupying employer can:

- be satisfied that the measures put in place by the visiting employer will not only protect visiting employees from exposure to the substances concerned, but also the occupier's employees;
- provide their employees with information and instruction about any hazardous substances that the visiting employer will be using or that the work will produce;
- reassure their employees that any exposure to the substances concerned and any risks to their health are being properly controlled.

People working under the control and direction of others

43   Only the courts can give an authoritative interpretation of the law. However, when deciding whether duties under COSHH apply, the following points should be considered:

- People working under the control and direction of others may be treated as self-employed for tax and national insurance purposes, but they may be treated as their employees for health and safety purposes.
- It may, therefore, be necessary to take appropriate action to protect them.
- If doubt exists about who is responsible for the health and safety of a worker, this could be clarified and included in the terms of a contract.

44   A legal duty under section 3 of the HSW Act cannot be passed on by means of a contract and there will still be duties towards others.

Regulation 4 Prohibitions relating to certain substances

(1)   Those substances described in Column 1 of Schedule 2 are prohibited to the extent set out in the corresponding entry in Column 2 of that Schedule.

(2)   The importation into the United Kingdom, other than from another member State, of the following substances and articles is prohibited, namely –

(a)   [Revoked by REACH Enforcement Regulations 2008/2852 Schedule 10(3), paragraph 6 (December 1, 2008),]
(b)   matches made with white phosphorus,

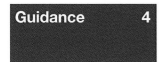

and a contravention of this paragraph shall be punishable under the Customs and Excise Management Act 1979 and not as a contravention of a health and safety regulation.

(3) A person shall not supply during the course of or for use at work a substance or article specified in paragraph (2).

(4) [Revoked by REACH Enforcement Regulations 2008/2852 Schedule 10(2), paragraph 1 (June 1, 2009).]

Guidance 4

45 HSE can grant exemptions from these prohibitions under regulation 15. However, it can only do so where it would not contravene requirements imposed by the European Union, and where it can be satisfied that people's health would not be affected as a result.

Regulation 5 Application of regulations 6 to 13

Regulation 5

(1) Regulations 6 to 13 shall have effect with a view to protecting persons against a risk to their health, whether immediate or delayed, arising from exposure to substances hazardous to health except –

(a) where and to the extent that the following Regulations apply, namely –
  (i) the Coal Mines (Control of Inhalable Dust) Regulations 2007;[a]
  (ii) the Control of Lead at Work Regulations 2002;
  (iii) the Control of Asbestos Regulations 2012;[b]
(b) where the substance is hazardous to health solely by virtue of its radioactive, explosive or flammable properties, or solely because it is at a high or low temperature or a high pressure;
(c) where the risk to health is a risk to the health of a person to whom the substance is administered in the course of his medical treatment.

(2) In paragraph (1)(c) "medical treatment" means medical or dental examination or treatment which is conducted by, or under the direction of a –

(a) registered medical practitioner;
(b) registered dentist; or
(c) other person who is an appropriate practitioner for the purposes of section 58 of the Medicines Act 1968,

and includes any such examination or treatment conducted for the purpose of research.

(a) Words substituted by the Coal Mines (Control of Inhalable Dust) Regulations 2007/1894 regulation 14(4) (October 1, 2007).
(b) Words substituted by the Control of Asbestos Regulations 2012/632 Schedule 3, paragraph 1 (April 6, 2012).

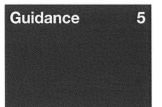

Other person who is an appropriate practitioner

46 The reference to the 'other person who is an appropriate practitioner' in regulation 5(2)(c) applies to people such as appropriate nurse practitioners, state registered chiropodists, registered midwives and people who hold a certificate of proficiency in ambulance paramedic skills etc who may prescribe certain medicines under the Prescription Only Medicines (Human Use) Order 1997.

Regulation 6 Assessment of the risk to health created by work involving substances hazardous to health

Regulation   6

(1) An employer shall not carry out work which is liable to expose any employees to any substance hazardous to health unless he has –

(a) made a suitable and sufficient assessment of the risk created by that work to the health of those employees and of the steps that need to be taken to meet the requirements of these Regulations; and

(b) implemented the steps referred to in sub-paragraph (a).

(2) The risk assessment shall include consideration of –

(a) the hazardous properties of the substance;

(b) information on health effects provided by the supplier, including information contained in any relevant safety data sheet;

(c) the level, type and duration of exposure;

(d) the circumstances of the work, including the amount of the substance involved;

(e) activities, such as maintenance, where there is the potential for a high level of exposure;

(f) any relevant workplace exposure limit or similar occupational exposure limit;

(g) the effect of preventive and control measures which have been or will be taken in accordance with regulation 7;

(h) the results of relevant health surveillance;

(i) the results of monitoring of exposure in accordance with regulation 10;

(j) in circumstances where the work will involve exposure to more than one substance hazardous to health, the risk presented by exposure to such substances in combination;

(k) the approved classification of any biological agent; and

(l) such additional information as the employer may need in order to complete the risk assessment.

(3) The risk assessment shall be reviewed regularly and forthwith if –

(a) there is reason to suspect that the risk assessment is no longer valid;

(b) there has been a significant change in the work to which the risk assessment relates; or

(c) the results of any monitoring carried out in accordance with regulation 10 show it to be necessary,

and where, as a result of the review, changes to the risk assessment are required, those changes shall be made.

(4) Where the employer employs 5 or more employees, he shall record –

(a) the significant findings of the risk assessment as soon as is practicable after the risk assessment is made; and

(b) the steps which he has taken to meet the requirements of regulation 7.

ACOP   6

COSHH risk assessment

47   Employers must not carry out work which can expose any of their employees to any substance hazardous to health until:

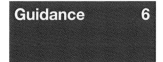

ACOP   6

- a suitable and sufficient assessment of the risks to employees' health created by that work has been carried out; and
- the steps needed to comply with the Regulations have been identified; and
- those steps have been put into operation.

Guidance   6

48   The purpose of the risk assessment is to enable employers to make valid decisions about the measures needed to prevent or adequately control the exposure of their employees to substances hazardous to health arising from the work.

ACOP   6

49   The risk assessment should take into account those substances which are:

- brought into the workplace and handled, stored and used for processing;
- produced or emitted, eg as fumes, vapour dust etc, by a process or an activity, or as a result of an accident or incident;
- used for, or arising from, maintenance, cleaning and repair work;
- produced at the end of any process, eg wastes, residues, scrap etc;
- produced from activities carried out by another employer's employees in the vicinity.

50   There may be situations where work is carried out before all the steps identified in the assessment are in place, eg engineering controls awaiting manufacture or installation, and significant reliance may be placed on the correct use of adequate and suitable personal protective equipment (PPE) during this interim period. Circumstances of this nature should be identified, justified and addressed in the assessment. When all the steps are fully implemented, the assessment should be reviewed and the outcome recorded, if appropriate.

The person who carries out the assessment

51   Employers must ensure that whoever carries out the assessment and provides information on the prevention and control measures is competent to do so (see regulation 7 of the MHSW Regulations and regulation 12(4) of COSHH).

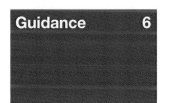

Guidance   6

52   The person carrying out the assessment may have access to people who can help to deliver the assessment and the implementation of the risk management measures. Employers should ensure everyone appointed to assist in meeting this requirement is competent to do the job and there is formal, written specification for the work that is being planned (see www.hse.gov.uk/business/competent-advice.htm).

ACOP   6

53   Where more than one person is involved in carrying out the assessment, the employer should nominate someone to co-ordinate, consult, compile, assure quality, record, communicate and implement the risk management measures and monitor their effectiveness, as well as consider the need for reviewing the assessment.

54   The competent person carrying out the assessment should:

- know how the work activity uses, produces or creates substances hazardous to health;
- have the knowledge, skills, training and experience to make sound decisions about the level of risk and the measures needed for prevention

ACOP   6

or adequate control of exposure;
- have the ability and the authority of the employer to collate all the necessary, relevant information.

Guidance   6

Suitable and sufficient risk assessment

55   The risk assessment should take into account the properties of the hazardous substance or biological agent, how and when they can give rise to risks to health, and the degree to which those risks need to be taken into account.

ACOP   6

56   Regulation 6(2)(a)–(l) requires the risk assessment to consider:

- the potential for the substance to cause harm from exposure by inhalation, ingestion, absorption, skin contact and infection (for a biological agent);
- the physical attributes of the substance, eg liquid, gas, mist, fume, dust or infective state, its ability to become airborne, and the means by which it could come into contact with the skin or other body membranes;
- the details of when and how exposure can occur and who may be affected, including workers and others;
- the effectiveness of existing controls and the options for improving control where prevention is not an option.

57   The risk assessment should consider *the work activity*, including:

- all the substances hazardous to health (including biological agents and simple asphyxiants) arising from the work (used, produced, synthesised, created as waste or by-products, or released from processes or during accidents, incidents and emergencies);
- work done by sub-contractors, at the workplace, that may expose employees to substances hazardous to health.

58   The risk assessment should consider *the hazards*, including:

- the physical, chemical and biological properties of the substances and the effects they could have on the body;
- where those substances are likely to be present and in what form, eg dust, vapour, mist, fume etc, and whether they are used or produced, and in what amounts and how often;
- the additional requirement regarding substances known, or suspected, to be carcinogens, mutagens or asthmagens, where there is a more compelling reason for the employer to substitute a less toxic alternative. Where this is not reasonably practicable, adequate procedures, training, instruction and supervision should ensure that the exposure level is reduced to as low a level as is reasonably practicable (ALARP).

59   The risk assessment should consider *the people exposed*, including:

- the ways in which, and the extent to which, any group of people (office staff, night cleaners, security guards, members of the public such as visitors, patients etc) could be exposed. For maintenance workers, where exposure may be foreseeably higher than normal, the type of work and process should be taken into account and any reasonably foreseeable deterioration, or failure, of any control measure provided;
- the need to protect particular groups of employees who may be at increased risk, eg inexperienced trainees and young people under 18; pregnant workers; disabled workers; and any employees known to be

ACOP   **6**

susceptible to certain illnesses such as dermatitis, asthma or other diseases which may be caused or made worse by exposure to substances hazardous to health.

60 The risk assessment should consider *types and extent of exposure*, including:

■ an estimate of exposure, taking into account any information available about:
- the concentration in air likely to be produced by the work concerned;
- the likelihood of skin contact;
- the effort needed to do the work and how this may affect the rate and volume of air employees breathe (for some work activities, employees might breathe three or four times the volume of air that they would breathe at rest);
- the effect of any engineering measures and systems of work currently used for controlling potential exposure;

■ a comparison between the estimate of exposure and any existing, valid standards which help to assess the adequacy of control, eg a WEL or 'biological monitoring guidance value';

■ the key points used to recognise and evaluate exposure in regulation 6(2)(a)–(l). Exposure through all routes must be considered (inhalation, skin contact, absorption through the skin and other body membranes, ingestion and puncture).

61 The risk assessment should consider *the potential health effects*, including:

■ the likelihood of a foreseeable risk of ill health (eg whether the risk is probable, possible, remote or nil/negligible);

■ the severity of ill health, if it occurs. This may be explained by the following three descriptors:
- serious health effects – permanent, progressive, irreversible, or permanently disabling conditions that result in lifelong disability or restriction to work, eg diseases such as silicosis, cancer, persistent occupational irritant contact dermatitis, sensitisation, asthma and serious chemical burns. These also include effects that would lead to loss of consciousness, eg from exposure to simple asphyxiants;
- significant health effects – non-permanent, reversible and non-progressive conditions that result in temporary disability, eg diseases such as salmonella, non-persistent occupational irritant contact dermatitis, farmers' lung and minor chemical burns to the skin;
- minor health effects – examples include temporary skin and respiratory irritation;

■ for potentially serious health effects, the risk assessment will need to be more comprehensive and the control measures more stringent to reduce exposure. For example, very toxic substances such as carcinogens require a more comprehensive assessment and a higher standard of control than low-toxicity substances such as mild irritants.

62 The risk assessment should consider *control measures*, including:

■ firstly, preventing exposure by substituting the hazardous substances or by using process design controls, if this is reasonably practicable;

■ if preventing exposure is not reasonably practicable, employers should consider controlling exposure adequately by using a less hazardous substance or a less hazardous form of the substance;

ACOP **6**

- the measures necessary to control exposure adequately could involve three approaches, to be used as appropriate and in accordance with the findings of the assessment, namely:
  - controls in the exposure pathway between the source and the worker, such as containment with integrated local exhaust ventilation (LEV) or using closed-loop transfer and sampling, fixed and portable LEV, or keeping a safe working distance;
  - worker-specific controls such as PPE and limiting the time exposed through worker rotation;
  - administrative controls, such as supervision and training;
- applying the principles of good practice in controlling exposure outlined in Schedule 2A and regulation 7;
- human factors. Human factors are critical because they can affect the use of controls and lead to unnecessary exposures. The issues include awareness, work rate and interaction with controls, including how easy they are to use. Employers should consider the way workers use the controls when making decisions about the design, installation and use of controls;
- the reasons for the chosen methods of avoiding or minimising the foreseeable risks, eg why substitution is not practicable when a carcinogen is used, or why PPE is used rather than engineering controls like LEV.

63 The risk assessment should also consider *other requirements*, including:

- correct use and efficient maintenance, examination and testing of control measures;
- exposure monitoring, where required;
- health surveillance, where required;
- provision of information, instruction and training;
- the ability to deal with accidents, incidents and emergencies;
- ensuring employees or their representatives are informed about the outcome of the assessment.

Assessing the risk from biological agents

64 Infection is dependent on a number of variable factors and not necessarily the amount of agent that is present. It is important to consider whether the work activity can provide a route by which the employee may be exposed to the biological agent. For exposure to biological agents, the employer should also consider:

- the hazard groups of any biological agents that may be present and what form they may be in, eg infectious stages or hardy spores;
- how and where they are present, how they are transmitted and the diseases they cause;
- the likelihood of exposure and consequent disease (including the identification of workers and non-workers, such as hospital patients, who may be particularly susceptible because, for example, they are immunocompromised), drawing on evidence of the prevalence of infection or other ill effect as experienced within a particular industry sector or workplace.

Guidance **6**

65 The level of risk should be the employer's main consideration and, even where the exposure is incidental to the activity, if the risk is sufficiently high and some of the measures listed in regulation 7(6) can reduce it, then the employer should apply those measures.

66 There is more detailed guidance about assessing the risks of exposure from biological agents in *Biological agents: Managing the risks in laboratories and healthcare premises*[7] and on HSE's biosafety webpages at www.hse.gov.uk/biosafety/infection.htm.

Obtaining information to help with the assessment of risks

67 It may be necessary to collect information on the properties and attributes of substances hazardous to health from a variety of sources to fully inform the assessment process.

Supplied chemicals and products

68 Employers should decide what information is required and the amount of detail needed to carry out the assessment. Safety data sheets for chemicals and products must be provided by the supplier to meet their legal responsibilities. These safety data sheets provide hazard/health effect details and the general precautions needed when handling a substance or product. The employer's knowledge and experience of the work activity and the circumstances of use will provide useful information for carrying out the assessment.

Information on natural substances, by-products, wastes etc

69 Substances hazardous to health generated when natural products are worked on (eg wood or stone), or produced as a by-product of the work (eg diesel engine exhaust fume, welding by-products and process wastes that may be gases, liquids or dusts), do not have safety data sheets. In these cases, employers should determine the hazardous properties, health effects and exposure patterns before embarking on an assessment. Employers can find hazard/health effects and control information for these types of substances from reliable sources such as HSE's *COSHH essentials* web tool (www.hse.gov.uk/coshh/essentials/) and other guidance material eg HSE webpages and guidance notes, manufacturers' standards, technical papers, trade association literature etc. Alternatively, they may seek advice from a competent person within or outside their organisation, eg a trade association.

Other information

70 HSE and industry publish a number of guidance and good practice standards to help employers control the risks from substances hazardous to health. Many of these are referenced in this document. Where chemicals are used in low-risk environments, employers may use HSE's *Health and safety made simple* webpages (www.hse.gov.uk/simple-health-safety/) to help with their assessment.

Implementing the steps to comply with the Regulations

71 Once employers have carried out the risk assessment and identified the steps required to:

- prevent or adequately control exposures;
- ensure correct use and efficient maintenance, examination and testing of the control measures;
- ensure that exposure monitoring and health surveillance are carried out, if required;
- ensure information and instruction are provided and training is carried out;

ACOP   6

- deal with accidents, incidents and emergencies;

the steps must be implemented before the work proceeds.

Guidance   6

72   To help implement the steps, employers could draw up a prioritised action plan detailing the steps required, timescales for action and giving details of the person or persons responsible for implementing each step of the plan.

Combining a COSHH risk assessment with other risk assessments

73   A COSHH assessment may be made as part of the general risk assessment duties placed on employers by regulation 3 of the MHSW Regulations 1999. In addition, where applicable, employers may combine the COSHH risk assessment with that required by regulation 5 of the DSEAR Regulations. If any of these actions are taken, employers should ensure that all assessments are suitable and sufficient to comply with relevant regulations.

ACOP   6

Exposure to two or more substances

74   Where a work activity may expose employees to more than one substance hazardous to health, the employer must consider the possible enhanced harmful effects of combined or sequential exposures.

75   If employees are under health surveillance which is being supervised by a doctor or other health professional, the employer should closely monitor the results for evidence of enhanced effects. Information may be available from other sources such as the individual suppliers of the substances, trade associations, guidance material or from the professional concerned.

Consulting employees and their representatives

76   When carrying out a suitable and sufficient risk assessment, the employer must consult employees and/or their safety representatives on any measures they plan to introduce as a result of the assessment which may substantially affect their health and safety. This is a legal requirement under the Safety Representatives and Safety Committees Regulations 1977 and the Health and Safety (Consultation with Employees) Regulations 1996.

Guidance   6

77   Consultation involves employers not only giving information to employees but also listening to them and taking account of what they say before making health and safety decisions. Issues employers must consult employees on include:

- risks arising from their work;
- proposals to manage and/or control these risks;
- the best ways of providing information and training.

78   Employers may wish to involve employees and/or safety representatives when carrying out and reviewing risk assessments as it's a good way of helping to manage health and safety risk. Employers could ask employees what they think the hazards are, as they may notice things that are not obvious and may have some good, practical ideas on how to control the risks.

ACOP   6

Recording the risk assessment

79   All employers must carry out a risk assessment but those employing five or more employees must also record any significant findings.

ACOP 6

80   The significant findings of the risk assessment should represent an effective statement of hazards, risks and actions taken to protect the health of employees and anyone else who may be affected by the work. Employers may use the recorded findings as evidence that:

■   they have carried out a suitable and sufficient assessment;
■   they have systematically considered all the factors relevant to the work, and put in place measures either to prevent exposure or to achieve and maintain adequate control of exposure.

81   The record may refer to, and rely on, other documents and records describing procedures and safeguards. It may be in writing or recorded by other means, eg electronically, so long as it is readily accessible and retrievable for use by employers in reviews or for examination by, for example, a safety representative or an inspector.

82   The amount of information employers record should be proportionate to the risks posed by the work. In the simplest and most obvious cases where a work activity involving exposure to a hazardous substance poses little or no risk, eg for many of the substances often found in small quantities in offices, the employer may need only record:

■   the substances to which the employees are or are likely to be exposed and the form in which they occur – liquid, powder, pellets, dust etc;
■   the measures taken to adequately control exposure, eg taking account of the information provided by the supplier, and using the substances in accordance with their accompanying instructions;
■   a statement to say that because the substances pose little or no risk, no further detailed risk assessment is necessary.

83   For exposure to substances that pose a small risk, the employer may group, on a single record, the combined assessment for a number of different low-risk hazardous substances. However, where the work concerned presents more of a risk to health, the significant findings of the assessment should comprise a more comprehensive record. It should include the appropriate items identified in paragraphs 57–63.

84   The record of the significant findings will also form the basis for a revision of the assessment.

Reviewing the risk assessment

85   The assessment should be reviewed immediately when there is evidence that it is no longer valid, for example:

■   deterioration in control effectiveness is identified from the results of exposure monitoring, or health surveillance, or the examination and testing of engineering controls;
■   following reports or complaints from supervisors, employees, maintenance staff, or safety representatives etc about defects in control measures;
■   changes to operating circumstances that have affected the control effectiveness and employees' exposure to substances hazardous to health, such as:
    –   new information on health effects;
    –   increase in productivity;
    –   changes to the hazardous substance (including its physical form, eg changing from powder to pellets);

ACOP   **6**

   – improvement to controls;
   – modification of the plant;
   – identification of susceptible individuals or loss of control effectiveness through health surveillance or exposure monitoring;
   – a new employee with no experience of the process.

86   Any significant findings from the review should be recorded, as applicable, and any revisions to the steps required to prevent or reduce exposure should be implemented.

Regulation 7 Prevention or control of exposure to substances hazardous to health

Regulation   **7**

(1)   Every employer shall ensure that the exposure of his employees to substances hazardous to health is either prevented or, where this is not reasonably practicable, adequately controlled.

(2)   In complying with his duty of prevention under paragraph (1), substitution shall by preference be undertaken, whereby the employer shall avoid, so far as is reasonably practicable, the use of a substance hazardous to health at the workplace by replacing it with a substance or process which, under the conditions of its use, either eliminates or reduces the risk to the health of his employees.

(3)   Where it is not reasonably practicable to prevent exposure to a substance hazardous to health, the employer shall comply with his duty of control under paragraph (1) by applying protection measures appropriate to the activity and consistent with the risk assessment, including, in order of priority –

(a)   the design and use of appropriate work processes, systems and engineering controls and the provision and use of suitable work equipment and materials;

(b)   the control of exposure at source, including adequate ventilation systems and appropriate organisational measures; and

(c)   where adequate control of exposure cannot be achieved by other means, the provision of suitable personal protective equipment in addition to the measures required by sub-paragraphs (a) and (b).

(4)   The measures referred to in paragraph (3) shall include –

(a)   arrangements for the safe handling, storage and transport of substances hazardous to health, and of waste containing such substances, at the workplace;

(b)   the adoption of suitable maintenance procedures;

(c)   reducing, to the minimum required for the work concerned –
   (i)   the number of employees subject to exposure;
   (ii)   the level and duration of exposure; and
   (iii)   the quantity of substances hazardous to health present at the workplace;

(d)   the control of the working environment, including appropriate general ventilation; and

(e)   appropriate hygiene measures including adequate washing facilities.

(5)   Without prejudice to the generality of paragraph (1), where it is not reasonably practicable to prevent exposure to a carcinogen or mutagen, the employer shall apply the following measures in addition to those required by

Regulation 7

paragraph (3) –

(a) totally enclosing the process and handling systems, unless this is not reasonably practicable;

(b) the prohibition of eating, drinking and smoking in areas that may be contaminated by carcinogens or mutagens;

(c) cleaning floors, walls and other surfaces at regular intervals and whenever necessary;

(d) designating those areas and installations which may be contaminated by carcinogens or mutagens and using suitable and sufficient warning signs; and

(e) storing, handling and disposing of carcinogens or mutagens safely, including using closed and clearly labelled containers.

(6)   Without prejudice to the generality of paragraph (1), where it is not reasonably practicable to prevent exposure to a biological agent, the employer shall apply the following measures in addition to those required by paragraph (3) –

(a) displaying suitable and sufficient warning signs, including the biohazard sign shown in Part IV of Schedule 3;

(b) specifying appropriate decontamination and disinfection procedures;

(c) instituting means for the safe collection, storage and disposal of contaminated waste, including the use of secure and identifiable containers, after suitable treatment where appropriate;

(d) testing, where it is necessary and technically possible, for the presence, outside the primary physical confinement, of biological agents used at work;

(e) specifying procedures for working with, and transporting at the workplace, a biological agent or material that may contain such an agent;

(f) where appropriate, making available effective vaccines for those employees who are not already immune to the biological agent to which they are exposed or are liable to be exposed;

(g) instituting hygiene measures compatible with the aim of preventing or reducing the accidental transfer or release of a biological agent from the workplace, including –

(i) the provision of appropriate and adequate washing and toilet facilities; and

(ii) where appropriate, the prohibition of eating, drinking, smoking and the application of cosmetics in working areas where there is a risk of contamination by biological agents; and

(h) where there are human patients or animals which are, or are suspected of being, infected with a Group 3 or 4 biological agent, the employer shall select the most suitable control and containment measures from those listed in Part II of Schedule 3 with a view to controlling adequately the risk of infection.

(7)   Without prejudice to the generality of paragraph (1), where there is exposure to a substance hazardous to health, control of that exposure shall only be treated as adequate if –

(a) the principles of good practice for the control of exposure to substances hazardous to health set out in Schedule 2A are applied;

(b) any workplace exposure limit approved for that substance is not exceeded; and

(c) for a substance –

(i) which carries the risk phrase R45, R46 or R49, or for a substance or process which is listed in Schedule 1; or

Regulation 7

(ii)   which carries the risk phrase R42 or R42/43, or which is listed in section C of HSE publication "Asthmagen? Critical assessments of the evidence for agents implicated in occupational asthma" as updated from time to time, or any other substance which the risk assessment has shown to be a potential cause of occupational asthma,
exposure is reduced to as low a level as is reasonably practicable.

(8)   [Revoked by the Control of Substances Hazardous to Health (Amendment) Regulations 2004/3386 regulation 2(d)(ii) (April 6, 2005).]

(9)   Personal protective equipment provided by an employer in accordance with this regulation shall be suitable for the purpose and shall –

(a)   comply with any provision in the Personal Protective Equipment Regulations 2002 which is applicable to that item of personal protective equipment; or
(b)   in the case of respiratory protective equipment, where no provision referred to in sub-paragraph (a) applies, be of a type approved or shall conform to a standard approved, in either case, by the Executive.

(10)   Without prejudice to the provisions of this regulation, Schedule 3 shall have effect in relation to work with biological agents.

(11)   In this regulation, "adequate" means adequate having regard only to the nature of the substance and the nature and degree of exposure to substances hazardous to health and "adequately" shall be construed accordingly.

ACOP 7

Prevention of exposure

87   An employer's overriding duty and first priority is to consider how to prevent employees being exposed to substances hazardous to health by all routes (regulation 7(1) and 7(2)). The duty to prevent exposure should be achieved by measures other than the use of PPE. Employers can best comply with this requirement by completely eliminating the use or production of substances hazardous to health in the workplace. This might be achieved by:

■   changing the method of work so that the operation giving rise to the exposure is no longer necessary; or
■   modifying a process to eliminate the production of a hazardous by-product or waste product; or
■   substituting, wherever reasonably practicable, a non-hazardous substance which presents no risk to health where a hazardous substance is used intentionally.

88   In many workplaces, it will not be possible or practicable to eliminate exposure to substances hazardous to health completely. Therefore, where it is necessary to use a hazardous substance, an employer should consider whether it is possible to reduce exposure and risk to the health of employees significantly by using:

■   an alternative, less hazardous substance; or
■   a different form of the same substance; or
■   a different process.

89   This can be achieved, for example, by using a substance in pellet form rather than powder so that exposure is negligible.

ACOP   **7**

90   Employers need to take into account the harmful properties of any proposed replacement substance. However, the harmful properties of many potential replacement substances may not all be known. Care should be taken when there are gaps in the knowledge about the potential of the substance to cause harm. The ultimate decision should be based on a balance of any new risks they might present against the potential benefits, taking into consideration all exposure routes. In considering potential substitutes, employers should be aware of the responsibilities they have under other regulations, eg DSEAR. For example, an employer's choice of a replacement substance with lower toxicity but higher flammability might increase the overall risk if the process has an intrinsic fire risk.

Adequate control of exposure

91   Where prevention of exposure to substances hazardous to health is not reasonably practicable, employers must comply with the duty in regulation 7(1) to control exposure adequately by all routes. To achieve this, employers must consider and apply, where appropriate for the circumstances of the work:

■   the measures set out in regulation 7(3) in the priority order given;
■   the specific measures in regulation 7(4);
■   the principles of good practice for the control of exposure to substances hazardous to health set out in Schedule 2A, as required by regulation 7(7)(a) (see paragraphs 99–119 for guidance on the principles);
■   any approved WEL for a substance hazardous to health in accordance with regulation 7(7)(b);
■   a reduction in exposure to ALARP for substances listed in regulation 7(7)(c).

92   The employer should apply the principles of good control practice (see paragraphs 99–119) in all circumstances, but it will not always be necessary to apply all the controls described in regulation 7(3) and (4). A combination of control measures will often be necessary to best protect the health of employees. The employer should give priority to those controls that contain or minimise the release of contaminants and the spread of hazardous substances into the workplace.

93   The employer should consider the way employees will use the controls when making decisions about their design, installation and use. Human factors, such as risk awareness, work rate, the design of the task and ease of use of controls, influence the extent of exposure to substances hazardous to health. Employers should also consider the arrangements for the safe handling, storage and transport of hazardous substances, of waste containing such substances, and suitable maintenance procedures etc. Employers should also make suitable arrangements for laundering contaminated clothing.

94   The specific standards that are needed to achieve adequate exposure control for each route of exposure, ie inhalation, skin and ingestion, are described in paragraphs 138–153.

95   Employers must also ensure that whoever provides advice on the prevention or control of exposure is competent to do (see regulation 7 of the MHSW Regulations and regulation 12(4) of COSHH). A competent person will have adequate knowledge, training and expertise, eg in the design of processes, control measures, including ventilation and PPE, the human and

technical reasons why these control measures can fail, and the importance of following the principles of good practice for the control of substances hazardous to health.

96 The requirement at regulation 7(4)(c)(iii) – 'reducing to the minimum required for the work concerned ... the quantity of substances hazardous to health present at the workplace' – is not intended to prevent employers buying hazardous substances in bulk to reduce their costs, but to reduce the overall risk by minimising the amount potentially released into the working area.

97 PPE must be used where it is not reasonably practicable to achieve adequate control of exposure by other control measures alone, and then only in addition to these control measures (regulation 7(3)(c) and Schedule 2A, Principle (d)).

98 Employers should ensure that the information, instruction and training given to employees, in accordance with regulation 12, cover all aspects of achieving and maintaining adequate control of exposure by all routes. In particular, employers should stress the importance of how the combination of good practice under regulation 7(7) and the protection measures the employer applies under regulation 7(3) are designed to protect employees' health from exposure to hazardous substances.

Principles of good practice for the control of substances hazardous to health

99 The objective of COSHH is to prevent, or adequately control, exposure to substances hazardous to health so as to prevent ill health. This guidance on good practice for the control of exposure to substances hazardous to health is to help employers after they have considered the duty in regulation 7(1) to prevent exposure.

100 Employers have a responsibility to manage and minimise the risks from work activities. They must develop suitable and sufficient control measures and ways of maintaining them. They should:

■ identify hazards and potentially significant risks;
■ take action to prevent and control risks;
■ keep control measures under regular review.

101 To be effective in the long term, control measures must be practical, workable and sustainable.

102 Good practice in the control of substances hazardous to health can be encapsulated in the eight generic principles set out in Schedule 2A. They must all be applied to obtain effective and reliable control. The principles overlap in their application. They are not ordered by rank – the first is not more important than the last – although there is a logic to their overall order of presentation. The principles are explained below:

Principle (a): Design and operate processes and activities to minimise emission, release and spread of substances hazardous to health
103 It is more effective, and usually cheaper, to reduce the emission of a contaminant at source, rather than to develop ways of removing the contaminant from the workplace once it has been released and dispersed. Sources of exposure should be reduced in number, size, emission or release rate as much as possible.

It is often not possible to obtain adequate and reliable control unless this is done. Both the processes and procedures need to be considered. To identify how people get exposed during work activities, it is essential to recognise the principal sources and how the contaminant is transferred within the workplace. Care should be taken to identify significant sources and causes of exposure.

Principle (b): Take into account all relevant routes of exposure – inhalation, skin and ingestion – when developing control measures

104 The physical, chemical and infectious properties of a substance, as it is used, have a great bearing on which route of exposure, or combination of routes, is most important. If there is no exposure, there is no risk to health; but usage nearly always leads to some exposure. Employers should consider:

■ the health effects that the substances can cause;
■ the way the substances are used;
■ the degree of exposure;
■ how exposure occurs.

Principle (c): Control exposure by measures that are proportionate to the health risk

105 The more severe the potential health effect, and the greater the likelihood of it occurring, the stricter the measures required to control exposure. Control measures that are adequate should take into account the nature and severity of the hazard and the magnitude, frequency and duration of exposure. They should be proportionate to the risk.

Principle (d): Choose the most effective and reliable control options that minimise the escape and spread of substances hazardous to health

106 Some control options are inherently more reliable and effective than others. For example, the protection afforded by PPE is highly dependent on good fit and attention to detail. In contrast, a very reliable form of control is changing the process so that less of the hazardous substance is emitted or released.

107 Employers should choose the most effective and reliable control options for the circumstances and direct these at the main sources and causes of exposure.

108 There is a broad hierarchy of control options available, based on inherent reliability and likely effectiveness. COSHH regulation 7 refers to many of these options. They include:

■ elimination of the hazardous substance;
■ modification of the substance, process and/or workplace;
■ applying controls to the process, such as enclosures, splashguards and LEV;
■ working in ways that minimise exposure, such as using a safe working distance to avoid skin exposure;
■ equipment or devices worn by exposed individuals.

109 The key message is that there is a hierarchy of reliability of control options and this is often linked to their effectiveness. There is good advice available on the engineering control aspects of control measures and the application of human factors principles (see References).

Principle (e): Where adequate control of exposure cannot be achieved by other means, provide, in combination with other control measures, suitable PPE

110 Effective control measures usually consist of a mixture of: process and/or workplace measures, applied controls (such as LEV), and methods of working that

minimise exposure and make the best use of controls. Sometimes the mix includes PPE, such as respirators, workwear or gloves.

111 PPE tends to be less effective and reliable than other control options because it:

- has to be selected for the individual;
- has to fit the individual and not interfere with their work or other PPE worn at the same time;
- has to be put on correctly every time it is worn;
- has to remain properly fitted all the time the individual is exposed;
- has to be properly stored, checked and maintained;
- tends to be delicate and relatively easily damaged;
- can fail without warning;
- may provide no protection when it fails.

Principle (f): Check and review regularly all elements of control measures for their continuing effectiveness

112 Once an effective set of workable control measures has been devised, it needs to be put in place and managed. This includes training all relevant people in the use and maintenance of the control measures. The requirement for maintenance covers all elements of the measures to get effective and sustained control of exposure. These include any defined methods of working, supervisory actions, record keeping etc (ie the 'software' of control) as well as the 'hardware' of control. Certainly, whatever hardware is involved must be checked and must continue to function as intended. But a similar approach needs to be taken to check the actions people must take and the methods of working they need to adopt. These need checking and correcting, if necessary, too.

113 The effectiveness of control measures should be checked regularly. Which checks, and how often they are made, will depend on the particular control measures and the consequences if the measures fail or degrade significantly. Process changes are likely to be more stable and reliable than, say, LEV. In turn, LEV is likely to be more stable and reliable than controls that rely on routine human behaviour.

Principle (g): Inform and train all employees on the hazards and risks from substances with which they work, and the use of control measures developed to minimise the risks

114 For control measures to be effective, people need to know how to use them properly. Most importantly, people need to know why it is necessary to work in a certain way and use the controls as specified – they need to be motivated.

115 Motivation comes from understanding what the health risks are and, therefore, why the control measures are important. It also comes from the user having confidence in the control measures and believing that they will protect his or her health.

116 If the health risk is serious, for example silicosis, cancer, asthma, allergic contact dermatitis or blood borne disease such as HIV, and is chronic or latent in nature, a good appreciation of the risk is especially important. With latent or delayed risks, exposure can often be excessive, with no short-term warning, such as smell or irritation, to indicate that anything is amiss. The people potentially exposed need to be told, clearly and honestly, why they should use the control measures and the potential consequences in terms of ill health if they do not use them.

Guidance   7

Principle (h): Ensure that the introduction of measures to control exposure does not increase the overall risk to health and safety

117 Process changes, enclosures, ventilation, new methods of working, PPE and other changes to control exposure can introduce new risks. For instance, process changes might mean that equipment cannot be fully decontaminated before maintenance staff are given repairs to do. Enclosures might create an explosion risk if they contain potentially explosive aerosols. New methods of working may create risks of musculoskeletal injury. LEV has to be maintained, introducing possible risks from access to, and manual handling of, heavy parts. PPE can restrict movement, feel and vision. And some controls may increase emissions to the environment.

118 People designing control measures should look for these 'new' risks and minimise them. They must not focus only on the risk from substances hazardous to health. A good control solution is one which minimises the health risk while reducing maintenance burdens, being relatively foolproof, and not introducing other risks (see regulation 3 of the MHSW Regulations).

119 Further information on good practice for the control of substances hazardous to health can be found at www.hse.gov.uk/coshh/.

ACOP   7

COSHH essentials
120 Employers may use the advice available from *COSHH essentials* (www.hse.gov.uk/coshh/essentials/) for identifying appropriate control measures for a wide range of hazardous substances/task combinations. It remains the responsibility of employers to ensure that they:

■ have made a suitable and sufficient assessment in accordance with regulation 6;
■ are controlling exposure adequately to substances hazardous to health in accordance with regulation 7(7);
■ are protecting employees' health.

121 Employers who use *COSHH essentials* may use the information as part of the significant findings of the assessment that they may need to record in accordance with regulation 6(4).

Guidance   7

122 COSHH requires exposure to substances hazardous to health encountered in the workplace to be adequately controlled. To achieve adequate control involves applying what is called 'good control practice', which is a consensus view of the hardware, systems of work and other measures that need to be put in place to control the risk. The flow diagram in Figure 1 illustrates the steps to follow to obtain advice on good control practice.

123 For simple tasks, with detailed guidance available on controls, employers may need to do little other than check that what they are doing follows the existing guidance. For more complex processes or tasks employers may need to use competent specialist help to identify the steps required to reduce exposure. Identifying, implementing and achieving control in these circumstances is likely to follow a more complex route.

Guidance 7

Figure 1 Route map for adequate control

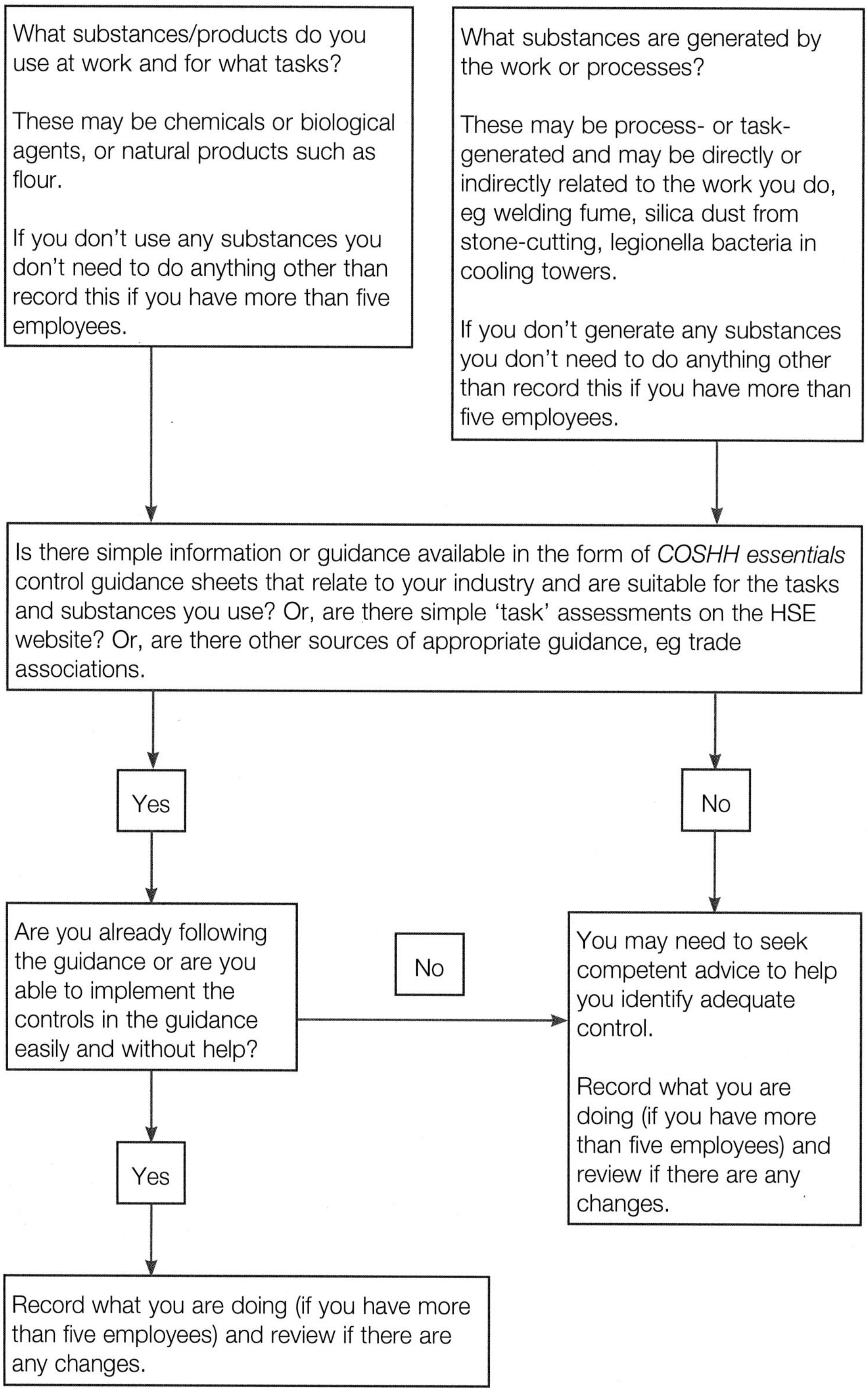

What substances/products do you use at work and for what tasks?

These may be chemicals or biological agents, or natural products such as flour.

If you don't use any substances you don't need to do anything other than record this if you have more than five employees.

What substances are generated by the work or processes?

These may be process- or task-generated and may be directly or indirectly related to the work you do, eg welding fume, silica dust from stone-cutting, legionella bacteria in cooling towers.

If you don't generate any substances you don't need to do anything other than record this if you have more than five employees.

Is there simple information or guidance available in the form of *COSHH essentials* control guidance sheets that relate to your industry and are suitable for the tasks and substances you use? Or, are there simple 'task' assessments on the HSE website? Or, are there other sources of appropriate guidance, eg trade associations.

Yes

No

Are you already following the guidance or are you able to implement the controls in the guidance easily and without help?

No

You may need to seek competent advice to help you identify adequate control.

Record what you are doing (if you have more than five employees) and review if there are any changes.

Yes

Record what you are doing (if you have more than five employees) and review if there are any changes.

| ACOP | 7 |

Control of exposure to carcinogens and mutagens

Prevention of exposure
124 An employer's first objective must be to prevent exposure to carcinogens or mutagens. Carcinogenic or mutagenic substances should not be used, or processes carried on, if the employer can use a suitable non-hazardous or less hazardous substitute. However, employers should take into account the toxic and other properties of possible chemical substitutes when considering changes.

Adequate control of exposure
125 If it is not reasonably practicable to prevent exposure to a carcinogen or mutagen, the employer must put into place all the measures in regulation 7(5) and appropriate controls set out in regulation 7(3). This means that whether or not it is reasonably practicable to totally enclose the process and handling systems in accordance with regulation 7(5)(a), all the other measures in 7(5)(b)–(e) are still required.

126 When synthesising chemicals, employers should choose routes which:

■ avoid, if possible, the use of carcinogenic or mutagenic substances at the start, or as part of any process or activity;
■ avoid, if possible, the formation of by-products, intermediates, wastes or residual contaminants consisting of, or containing, carcinogenic or mutagenic substances.

Use, storage, labelling and disposal
127 Employers should:

■ keep carcinogenic or mutagenic substances to be used in the workplace to the minimum needed for the process and, where appropriate, store and transport them on site in closed containers, clearly labelled and with clearly visible warning and hazard signs. However, there may be circumstances where, to ensure the adequate control of exposure, it is preferable to store a larger quantity in a controlled manner than to deal with frequent supplies of smaller volume;
■ clearly label and securely store carcinogenic or mutagenic waste products until they are removed by a competent specialist contractor, or disposed of safely on site by incineration or in some other way that does not put employees at risk or contaminate the outside environment;
■ clearly identify the areas in which exposure to carcinogens or mutagens may occur and take measures to prevent the spread of contamination within and beyond these areas. The number of people likely to be exposed to carcinogenic or mutagenic substances and the duration of their exposure must be kept to the minimum necessary for the work. Non-essential personnel must be excluded.

Precautions against contamination
128 Where there is a risk of an area being contaminated by a carcinogenic or mutagenic substance, employers should ensure that:

■ employees do not eat, drink, smoke or apply cosmetics in the areas concerned;
■ appropriate warning signs are prominently displayed;
■ where areas are set aside for employees and others to eat, drink and smoke, they should be without risk of being contaminated by a carcinogenic or mutagenic substance;

ACOP   **7**

- appropriate hygiene measures are in place, including cleaning procedures to remove any contamination from walls, doors, tools, equipment, clothing, PPE, other surfaces etc;
- adequate washing facilities are provided so that employees who are exposed to a carcinogen or mutagen can maintain a high standard of personal hygiene. This is consistent with the need to ensure adequate control of exposure and to avoid the spread of carcinogenic or mutagenic substances.

Control of exposure to biological agents

129 If employers cannot prevent exposure to a biological agent they should take steps to ensure that it is controlled adequately and consider all the requirements set out in regulation 7(3), (4), (6) and (7). They should apply the principles of good practice and use each requirement where, and to the extent that:

- it is applicable;
- the assessment carried out under regulation 6 shows that it will lead to a reduction in risk.

Deliberate work
130 Deliberate work with a biological agent should be carried out in contained-use facilities. Schedule 3 to these Regulations sets out the containment measures required to ensure that agents are not transmitted to workers or released outside the containment facility. When working with an agent in a particular hazard group, the containment level selected (which incorporates the required containment measures from regulation 7(6)) must match the hazard group of the agent as a minimum.

131 Some of the containment measures in Schedule 3 may be needed when nursing patients (animal or human) that are infected, or suspected of being infected, with the highest risk biological agents (Hazard Group 3 or 4).

132 Schedule 3 requires that biological agents are suitably classified and notified, where appropriate, and that exposure records are kept for persons working with Hazard Group 3 or 4 biological agents.

Incidental exposure
133 If the risk assessment concludes that exposure to a biological agent is unavoidable, but it is incidental to the main purpose of the work and the risk is low, then not all the measures in regulation 7(6) will need to be adopted.

Immunisation
134 If the risk assessment concludes there is a risk of exposure to biological agents for which effective vaccines are readily available, these should be offered. It is recommended that employers keep a vaccination record. The HSW Act requires that the employer provides protective measures such as immunisation to workers free of charge.

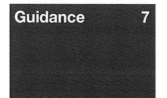

Guidance   **7**

135 The advantages and disadvantages of immunisation versus non-immunisation should be explained when making the offer. Immunisation should be seen only as a useful supplement to reinforce physical and procedural control measures, not as the sole protective measure.

136 Employees may not wish to take up the offer of immunisation, or they may not respond to a vaccine and will, therefore, not be immune. If so, employers should

Guidance 7

consider the effectiveness of the other controls and consider whether any additional controls should be implemented to allow them to work safely.

137 More detailed guidance is available from the Advisory Committee on Dangerous Pathogens or HSE's biosafety webpages (www.hse.gov.uk/biosafety) about controlling the risks from biological agents.

Adequate control for exposure by inhalation

Workplace exposure limits (WELS)

138 HSE has established WELs for a number of substances hazardous to health. These are intended to prevent excessive exposure to specified hazardous substances by containing exposure below a set limit. A WEL is the maximum concentration of an airborne substance averaged over a reference period to which employees may be exposed by inhalation.

139 WELs should not be considered a hard and fast line between safe and unsafe. The principles of good control practice require the degree to which exposure is reduced below the WEL to be proportionate to the health risk. If employers apply the principles of good practice for the control of substances hazardous to health correctly, exposure should be below any relevant WEL.

140 WELs refer to concentrations of hazardous substances in the air that people breathe, averaged over a specified period of time referred to as a time-weighted average (TWA). Two time periods are used: long-term (eight hours), and short-term (15 minutes). These limits cannot be readily adapted to evaluate or control non-occupational exposure.

141 Some substances for which WELs have been approved have been assigned short-term exposure limits (STELs) and have a 15-minute reference period. These substances can have acute effects and the purpose of the short-term limit is to protect against the adverse health effect occurring from brief exposures to the substance.

142 HSE's publication EH40/2005 *Workplace exposure limits* includes the list of substances assigned a WEL. It also provides more detailed guidance on the use of WELs. This includes the approved methods for averaging over the specified reference periods an explanation of the terms 'respirable' and 'inhalable' and related material.

ACOP 7

Substances defined as carcinogens, mutagens or a cause of occupational asthma and assigned a WEL
143 Where the health effects arising from exposure are more serious, such as cancer or asthma, then there needs to be a high standard of control. The extent to which employers should reduce exposure below the WEL depends on the degree of risk presented by the substance, weighed against the cost and effort involved in taking measures to reduce the risk. Employers should continue to reduce exposure to ALARP. This means improving control until the cost of further reduction in exposure becomes grossly disproportionate when weighed against the benefit gained.

144 If an individual develops occupational asthma due to exposure to a substance, their exposure must be controlled to prevent triggering further attacks. Suitable levels are likely to be well below any WEL, where these exist.

ACOP   **7**

145 To comply with the requirements in regulation 7(7)(c), employers may have to carry out a programme of exposure monitoring in accordance with regulation 10, unless the risk assessment made under regulation 6 shows that the level of exposure is most unlikely ever to exceed the WEL.

Other substances assigned a WEL
146 For a substance assigned a WEL that is not classified under COSHH as a carcinogen, mutagen, or a cause of occupational asthma, adequate control of exposure will be achieved by applying the principles of good practice for the control of exposure to the work involving the substance concerned. This applies particularly to the requirement to reduce exposure in proportion to the health risk and below any WEL.

Inhaled substances not assigned WELs
147 The absence of a substance from the list of WELs does not mean that it is safe. Many substances do not have a WEL. For these substances, employers should apply the principles of good practice to control exposure to a level to which nearly all the working population could be exposed, day after day at work, without adverse effects on health.

148 If it is not possible to identify suitable exposure control measures using, for instance, *COSHH essentials*, and no WEL exists, it may be possible and useful for the employer to identify or develop an in-house exposure standard. Suppliers, trade associations or specialist advisers, eg occupational hygienists, may be able to help.

Adequate control of exposure by routes other than inhalation

149 COSHH requires that employers prevent or control exposure adequately by all routes, not just the inhalation route, and deal with substances which can be hazardous to health by:

■ absorption through the skin or mucous membranes;
■ contact with the skin or mucous membranes, eg dermatitis, chemical burns and microbial infection;
■ ingestion;
■ skin puncture.

Exposure via the skin (or mucous membranes or eyes)
150 Some substances can pass though the skin (eg those with a Sk notation in *Workplace exposure limits*) and cause diseases in other parts of the body. Other substances can cause 'local effects', which are limited to the skin itself. For example, corrosive substances may lead to burns; irritant substances may lead to contact dermatitis; other substances may lead to skin allergies or skin cancer.

151 Where employers identify a skin contamination problem, they should develop measures to adequately control the risk. The principles of good practice should be applied to achieve adequate control of exposure to skin and eyes. In addition to the specific control measures set out in paragraphs 87–98, skin care will help to protect the skin by reducing the effects of exposure. Skin care includes prompt removal of accidental contamination, good personal hygiene and the use of appropriate emollients. HSE's *Managing skin exposure risks at work*[8] provides further guidance.

Exposure through ingestion
152 Examples of when ingestion can occur include:

ACOP   7

- transfer from clothing onto food;
- inadvertent hand-to-mouth contact;
- employees who do not wash their hands and face before eating.

153 Where substances potentially hazardous by ingestion are used, employers should ensure that employees remove any contaminated clothing in the area set aside for this activity, thoroughly wash their hands and face and under their fingernails before eating, drinking or smoking. Employers should stress the importance of employees following good personal hygiene practices and of not eating food in the work area.

Guidance   7

154 HSE publishes good practice advice to help employers decide on suitable control measures, including HSE's *COSHH essentials* webpages, which offer hazard-specific and task-specific guidance for a number of common processes at www.hse.gov.uk/coshh/essentials/. Employers can obtain information about substances from a number of other sources, including:

- manufacturers and suppliers of the substance;
- industry associations;
- occupational medicine and occupational hygiene journals.

When PPE might be necessary

155 Regulation 7(3)(c) and Principle (e) in Schedule 2A require the employer to provide employees with suitable PPE, eg respiratory protective equipment (RPE), protective clothing, protective gloves, footwear, and equipment to protect the eyes. This is in addition to all other control measures if the combination of those measures fails to achieve adequate control of exposure. The employer must not charge the worker for PPE, which is provided in order to comply with these Regulations (section 9 of the HSW Act).

ACOP   7

156 The situations where PPE will normally be necessary include:

- where adequate control of exposure cannot be achieved solely by good practice and the application of operational or engineering measures appropriate to the activity and consistent with the risk assessment. In this case, suitable PPE should be used in addition to those measures to secure adequate control;
- where a new or revised assessment shows that PPE is necessary until adequate control is achieved by other measures;
- where there is temporary failure to achieve adequate control of the process, eg because of plant failure. In this case, suitable PPE should be used as the only practicable solution for reimposing adequate control in the time available;
- where maintenance has to be carried out and the risk of exposure is assessed and appropriate control, such as prior decontamination of equipment and areas, is identified and carried out. In this case, although exposure may occur regularly, its infrequency and the small number of people involved, as well as the difficulties of applying process and engineering controls, often make the use of PPE necessary.

157 In assessing whether the use of PPE is the appropriate option, employers should consider:

- the type and level of exposure to the hazardous substance concerned;
- its effectiveness in the actual work situation;
- the practical difficulties of ensuring its continued correct use;

ACOP   **7**

- the limitations;
- the costs.

Suitable PPE

158 PPE should control adequately the hazardous substances to which the wearer is exposed, or is liable to be exposed, throughout the time it is used. When selecting PPE it is important for employers to take into account:

- the circumstances in which it will be used, eg the substances to which it will be exposed and for how long, and the degree of protection necessary;
- whether it can resist penetration and permeation by the substance concerned for a specified or recommended period;
- whether the design is adequate and suitable, ie the equipment fits the wearer, does not dislodge, deform, melt or otherwise fail to perform in the conditions in which it is used, and is compatible with other PPE worn;
- the environment in which it will be worn and, in dusty environments, whether the materials the PPE is made from reduce the tendency for dust to collect on the PPE and be re-released;
- the need to clean and check PPE regularly to ensure that it remains effective.

159 Manufacturers of PPE must ensure that their products comply with the Personal Protective Equipment Regulations 2002.

Suitable RPE

160 For each work activity for which it is foreseen that employees will need to wear RPE, the employer should specify the suitable equipment to be worn to make sure that employees are given adequate protection. To be suitable, RPE must be capable of adequately controlling the inhalation exposure using as a guide the equipment's assigned protection factor as listed in HSE's *Respiratory protective equipment at work*.[9] In selecting and providing suitable RPE, consider:

- the level of protection claimed by manufacturers for different types of RPE, and identify those types that will provide the appropriate protection for the likely or known exposure;
- the type of work to be done; the physical effort required to do it; the length of time the RPE will have to be worn; the requirements for visibility, comfort and employee communication; its compatibility with any other PPE that may be needed (eg safety glasses). In addition, the RPE must be matched to the job and the environment in which it is to be used;
- the fit for the wearer. Tight-fitting RPE (ie full and half masks) should be face-fit tested, using a suitable method, by a competent person (see regulation 7 of the MHSW Regulations and regulation 12(4) of COSHH). Fit testing will need to be repeated when there is any change in equipment or the facial characteristics of the wearer that could affect the fit. Loose-fitting devices, such as powered respirators with a visor or hood, need not be face-fit tested but still need to fit observably close to the face;
- the presence of a 'CE' mark showing that it is manufactured to meet minimum legal requirements, or (if the Personal Protective Equipment Regulations 2002 do not apply to the RPE in question) is of a type

ACOP   7

approved by, or conforms to a standard approved by HSE;

- the proper training and supervision of employees in its use. This will include wearers being clean-shaven in the area of the face seal when using tight-fitting RPE;
- regular cleaning, checking and maintenance to ensure that it remains effective.

Guidance   7

161 Consulting wearers on the selection of suitable equipment will help ensure that they have the most comfortable equipment best suited for them, which, as a consequence, is more likely to be worn and used correctly.

162 More information about fit testing can be found at www.hse.gov.uk/respiratory-protective-equipment.

ACOP   7

Facilities for washing, changing, eating and drinking

163 Employers should provide facilities to:

- ensure that employees meet and maintain a standard of personal hygiene that is consistent with adequate control of exposure;
- avoid the spread of substances hazardous to health;
- reduce the risk of ingestion of substances hazardous to health.

164 The facilities should include:

- adequate washing facilities. These should be in a convenient position but situated so that they do not themselves become contaminated. The facilities provided should relate to the type and level of exposure;
- changing facilities. These should be provided when PPE is used or where outdoor clothing could be contaminated by substances hazardous to health. They should be located and designed to prevent the spread of contamination from protective clothing to personal clothing and from one facility to another; also to prevent contamination from getting on to the RPE from other equipment or protective clothing;
- facilities for eating, drinking etc. Employees should not eat, chew, drink or smoke in places that are contaminated by substances hazardous to health. This will help reduce the risk of employees ingesting hazardous substances. If employers have to prohibit eating, drinking etc in certain areas, they should set aside an uncontaminated area or areas where these activities can be carried out. Access to the eating area should be convenient from both the working area and washing facilities.

165 Employers should ensure that not only are personal hygiene measures provided, but also that employees are made aware, through information, instruction and training, of why, how and when they must be used. Employers should also ensure, through appropriate supervision, that employees use the facilities in accordance with agreed procedures.

Guidance   7

166 Employers may also have duties under the Workplace (Health, Safety and Welfare) Regulations 1992 to provide the facilities described above.

Regulation 8 Use of control measures etc

Regulation	8

(1) Every employer who provides any control measure, other thing or facility in accordance with these Regulations shall take all reasonable steps to ensure that it is properly used or applied as the case may be.

(2) Every employee shall make full and proper use of any control measure, other thing or facility provided in accordance with these Regulations and, where relevant, shall –

(a) take all reasonable steps to ensure it is returned after use to any accommodation provided for it; and

(b) if he discovers a defect therein, report it forthwith to his employer.

ACOP	8

Employers' duties

167 Employers should establish procedures to ensure that control measures, including PPE and any other item or facility, are properly used or applied and are not made less effective by other work practices or by improper use. The procedures should include:

■ visual checks and observations at appropriate intervals;
■ ensuring that where more than one item of PPE is being worn, the different items are compatible;
■ supervising employees to ensure that the defined methods of work are being followed;
■ monitoring systems for the effectiveness of controls and prompt remedial action where necessary.

Employees' duties

168 Employees should use the control measures in the way they are intended to be used and as they have been instructed. In particular, they should:

■ use the control measures provided for materials, plant and processes;
■ follow the defined methods of work;
■ wear the PPE provided, including any RPE, correctly and in accordance with the manufacturer's instructions;
■ store the PPE, when not in use, in the accommodation provided;
■ remove any PPE which could cause contamination before eating, drinking or smoking;
■ maintain a high standard of personal hygiene and make proper use of the facilities provided for washing, showering or bathing and for eating and drinking;
■ report promptly to the appointed person, eg 'foreman', supervisor or safety representative, any defects discovered in any control measure, including defined methods of work, device or facility, or any PPE, including RPE.

Regulation 9 Maintenance, examination and testing of control measures

Regulation	9

(1) Every employer who provides any control measure to meet the requirements of regulation 7 shall ensure that –

Regulation   9

(a)   *in the case of plant and equipment, including engineering controls and personal protective equipment, it is maintained in an efficient state, in efficient working order, in good repair and in a clean condition; and*

(b)   *in the case of the provision of systems of work and supervision and of any other measure, it is reviewed at suitable intervals and revised if necessary.*

(2)   *Where engineering controls are provided to meet the requirements of regulation 7, the employer shall ensure that thorough examination and testing of those controls is carried out –*

(a)   *in the case of local exhaust ventilation plant, at least once every 14 months, or for local exhaust ventilation plant used in conjunction with a process specified in Column 1 of Schedule 4, at not more than the interval specified in the corresponding entry in Column 2 of that Schedule; or*

(b)   *in any other case, at suitable intervals.*

(3)   *Where respiratory protective equipment (other than disposable respiratory protective equipment) is provided to meet the requirements of regulation 7, the employer shall ensure that thorough examination and, where appropriate, testing of that equipment is carried out at suitable intervals.*

(4)   *Every employer shall keep a suitable record of the examinations and tests carried out in accordance with paragraphs (2) and (3) and of repairs carried out as a result of those examinations and tests, and that record or a suitable summary thereof shall be kept available for at least 5 years from the date on which it was made.*

(5)   *Every employer shall ensure that personal protective equipment, including protective clothing, is:*

(a)   *properly stored in a well-defined place;*
(b)   *checked at suitable intervals; and*
(c)   *when discovered to be defective, repaired or replaced before further use.*

(6)   *Personal protective equipment which may be contaminated by a substance hazardous to health shall be removed on leaving the working area and kept apart from uncontaminated clothing and equipment.*

(7)   *The employer shall ensure that the equipment referred to in paragraph (6) is subsequently decontaminated and cleaned or, if necessary, destroyed.*

Guidance   9

General

169   The objective of this regulation is to ensure that every element of a control measure performs as originally intended, and continues to adequately control the exposure of employees to substances hazardous to health. This includes the identification of any significant deterioration in any element of the control measure, and the taking of any necessary corrective steps. The frequency of any checks carried out will depend on the likelihood of significant deterioration of that particular element of the control measure and its importance. In any event, it should be done at intervals of not more than one year and after any incidents.

170   'Maintenance' means any work carried out to sustain the efficiency of control measures, and not just carried out by maintenance workers. It includes visual checks on any equipment relevant to the control of exposure, inspection, servicing,

Guidance 9

observation of systems of work, and any remedial work to maintain the effectiveness of control measures. The requirement for maintenance is restricted to control of exposure, so that the duty to maintain control measures no longer applies when people are not exposed to substances hazardous to health, eg during periods when a process is shut down.

171 Anyone who checks the effectiveness of any element of a control measure should have the competence to do so. The degree of theoretical and practical knowledge required will increase with the likelihood of control failure, the seriousness of the consequences, and the complexity of the control measure.

Maintenance of all control measures

172 All control measures in use should be visually checked, where possible, at appropriate intervals and without undue risk to maintenance staff. In the case of LEV and work enclosures, such checks should be carried out at least once a week.

173 Procedures for servicing equipment should specify:

- which control measures need servicing;
- the work to be carried out on each of them;
- when the work should be done;
- who is to do the work and who is responsible for it;
- how to put right any defects found.

ACOP 9

174 In most circumstances, control measures will include defined working procedures. These should be observed regularly to check that they are still being followed. They should also be reviewed periodically to confirm that they are still appropriate and workable, and to see whether they can be improved.

175 Employers must ensure that whoever carries out maintenance, examinations and tests is competent to do so (see regulation 7 of the MHSW Regulations and regulation 12(4) of COSHH). People carrying out examinations and tests on control measures such as LEV and PPE must have adequate knowledge, training and expertise in examination methods and techniques.

Control measures subject to thorough examinations and tests

Engineering controls
176 In all cases, engineering control measures provided to control exposure must be thoroughly examined and tested at suitable or specified intervals. This is to ensure that they are continuing to perform as intended.

177 Employers should check all engineering controls when they are installed to ensure that they meet the specified technical performance and, in combination with other control measures, are capable of providing adequate control. This initial, or commissioning, information can provide a benchmark for subsequent regular examinations and tests. The results of each thorough examination and test should be checked against the assessment carried out under regulation 6 and the requirements of regulation 7 regarding control. Any defects found as a result of the examinations or tests should be put right as soon as possible.

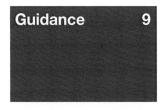

178 The form of the thorough examinations and tests will depend on:

■ the particular engineering control under consideration, ie its inherent reliability in sustaining the level of control over the hazardous substance concerned;
■ the type and the extent of the risk posed by the hazardous substance, ie the consequences of deterioration or failure of the control measure.

ACOP 9

179 In the case of LEV plant, the requirements set out in paragraph 185 should be met. For all other engineering controls, the examinations and tests should be sufficient to reveal any defect or latent defect.

Frequency of examination and testing

180 The frequency of examinations or tests should also be linked to the type of engineering control in use, the extent of any risk in the event of its failure or deterioration, and the likelihood that failure or deterioration will occur.

181 The frequency may need to be increased alongside the age of the engineering control concerned. There may also be the need to re-examine and reassess the frequency of examinations and tests in the event of any significant change to the plant or process. For LEV, the frequency of the thorough examinations and tests is specified in regulation 9(2)(a) and Schedule 4.

182 Where the control measures are important for preventing sudden or serious effects on people, eg flexible connections for delivery of toxic fluids, or extraction ventilation for processes emitting toxic fumes, the inspection needs to be very frequent and, in the case of controls used only occasionally, before each use. Condition monitoring, eg air flow sensors in extraction ducts, may need to be continuous and linked to alarms. Air sensor operation may also be needed to detect hazardous substances and raise an alarm if a pre-set limit is breached. All such arrangements should emerge from the risk assessment.

183 Employers and employees should give the person carrying out the thorough examinations and tests all the co-operation needed for the work to be carried out correctly and fully.

Suitable records

184 Employers should keep a suitable record in respect of each thorough examination and test. For LEV plant, the record should contain the information listed in paragraph 186. For all other engineering controls, employers should keep similar information, but adapt it so that it is relevant to the type of engineering control concerned.

Local exhaust ventilation

185 The examination and test should ensure that the LEV plant can meet its intended operating performance for adequately controlling hazardous substances for the purposes of regulation 7. This applies whether the LEV is fixed or portable; it includes microbiological safety cabinets, external high-efficiency particulate arrester (HEPA) filters fitted as part of extraction systems in laboratories and on-tool extraction systems. By following the guidance set out in HSE's *Controlling airborne contaminants at work*[10] and at www.hse.gov.uk/lev/, employers can help to ensure that the examination and

ACOP 9

testing of their LEV systems are carried out in accordance with the requirements of regulation 9(2).

186 A suitable employer record in respect of each thorough examination and test of LEV should normally contain the following details:

- the name and address of the employer responsible for the LEV;
- the date of the thorough examination and test;
- the date of the last thorough examination and test;
- the identification and location of the LEV, and the process and hazardous substance concerned;
- the operating conditions at the time of the test and whether this was normal production or special conditions;
- a simple diagram of the LEV layout and location, with test points;
- the general condition of the LEV system, including hood serial numbers and, where appropriate, photographs of relevant parts;
- information about the LEV plant which shows:
  - its intended operating performance for adequately controlling the hazardous substance for the purposes of regulation 7. (Note: If there is no information available on this, it indicates a need for a further assessment in accordance with regulation 6 to show compliance with regulation 7);
  - whether the plant is still achieving the same performance;
  - if not, the adjustments, modifications or repairs needed to achieve that performance;
- the methods used to judge performance and the action to be taken to achieve that performance, eg visual, smoke test, airflow measurements, pressure measurements, dust lamp, air sampling, tests to check the condition and effectiveness of the filter;
- the results of any air sampling relevant to LEV performance;
- information on the way operators use the LEV;
- information on general system wear and tear and whether components may need repair or replacement before the next test;
- the name, job title and employer of the person carrying out the examination and test;
- the signature of the person carrying out the examination and test;
- the details of any minor adjustments or repairs carried out to make the LEV system effective;
- the details of any critical defects identified.

187 Employers should address critical defects immediately to ensure adequate control.

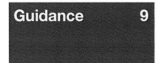

Guidance 9

188 The list above is not definitive and inclusion of all points may not be appropriate for all types of LEV. Further information on suitable thorough examination and test records can be found on the LEV webpages at www.hse.gov.uk/lev/.

ACOP 9

189 Examples of the information which should be available in respect of the main components of the LEV system include:

- enclosures/hoods: maximum number to be in use at any one time; location or position; static pressure behind each hood or extraction point; and face velocity;
- ducting: dimensions; transport velocity; and volume flow;
- filter/collector: specification; volume flow; static pressure at inlet, outlet and across filter;

ACOP   9

- fan or air mover: specification; volume flow; static pressure at inlet; and direction of rotation;
- systems which return exhaust air to the workplace: filter efficiency; and concentration of contaminant in returned air.

Respiratory protective equipment

190 The maintenance, examinations and tests of RPE should be in accordance with the manufacturer's instructions. Examinations should comprise a thorough visual examination of all parts of the respirator or breathing apparatus to ensure that all parts are present, correctly fitted, and the equipment is in good working order. In particular, the examination should ensure that the straps, facepieces, filters and valves are sound and in good working condition. For powered respirators, tests should:

- be made on the condition and efficiency of those parts;
- ensure that the battery pack is in good condition;
- ensure that the respirator delivers at least the manufacturer's recommended minimum volume flow rate.

191 For constant flow airline and demand valve breathing apparatus, tests should include the pressure in the air cylinders and the volume flow rate.

192 The quality of the air supplied to breathing apparatus should be tested at suitable intervals, depending on the task and the frequency of use. When the air supply is from mobile compressors, the employer should ensure that, wherever a compressor is located, the quality of air it supplies is not compromised by nearby contaminants. In every case, the air supplied to breathing apparatus should meet the relevant quality standard. As it is not reasonably practicable to test for all contaminants, the risk assessment made under regulation 6 should guide what other contaminants will require testing for.

Frequency of examinations and tests

193 Thorough maintenance examinations and, where appropriate, tests of items of RPE, other than disposable respirators, should be made at suitable intervals. The frequency should increase where the health risks and conditions of exposure are particularly severe.

194 In situations where RPE is used only occasionally, an examination and test should be made before their next use and maintenance carried out as appropriate. The person who is responsible for managing the maintenance of RPE should determine suitable intervals between examinations. Emergency escape-type RPE should be examined and tested in accordance with the manufacturer's instructions.

195 Suitable arrangements should be made to ensure that no employee uses RPE previously used by another person, unless it has been thoroughly washed and cleaned in accordance with the manufacturer's instructions.

Suitable records

196 The record of each thorough examination and test of RPE carried out should include:

- the name and address of the employer responsible for the RPE;

ACOP 9

- particulars of the equipment and of the distinguishing number or mark, together with a description sufficient to identify it, and the name of the maker;
- the date of examination and the name and signature or other acceptable means of identifying the person carrying out the examination and test;
- the condition of the equipment and details of any defect found, including, for canister or filter respirators, the state of the canister and the condition of the filter;
- for constant flow airline and demand valve breathing apparatus, the pressure of air/gas in the supply cylinder;
- for powered respirators and breathing apparatus, the volume flow rate to ensure that they can deliver at least the manufacturer's minimum recommended flow rate;
- the results of any breathing air quality tests.

Keeping records

197 Employers may keep records in any format, eg on paper or electronically. Records should be kept readily accessible and retrievable at any reasonable time for examination by safety representatives or inspectors etc.

Guidance 9

Accommodation for, and checking of, PPE

198 Employers should ensure that accommodation is provided for PPE so that it can be safely stored or kept when it is not in use. The adequacy of the accommodation will vary according to the quantity, type and its use, eg pegs, (labelled) lockers, shelves or containers etc. The storage should be adequate to protect the PPE from contamination, loss or damage by, for example, harmful substances, damp or sunlight.

199 Where quantities of PPE are stored, equipment which is ready for use should be clearly segregated from that which is awaiting repair or maintenance. Where PPE becomes contaminated during use, and especially by biological agents, the accommodation should be separate from any the employer provides for ordinary clothing and equipment. Employers may also have duties under the Workplace (Health, Safety and Welfare) Regulations 1992 to provide accommodation for PPE.

200 All PPE should be checked regularly to ensure that it continues to function and provide protection. The types of checks should be suited to that item of PPE and be able to detect significant deterioration. The more likely the performance of a particular item of PPE is to deteriorate, the more often it needs checking. Whoever does this work should be sufficiently knowledgeable and trained to identify deterioration and significant faults. Equipment that has deteriorated significantly or is faulty should be effectively repaired or disposed of safely.

Regulation 10 Monitoring exposure at the workplace

Regulation 10

(1) Where the risk assessment indicates that –

(a) it is requisite for ensuring the maintenance of adequate control of the exposure of employees to substances hazardous to health; or

(b) it is otherwise requisite for protecting the health of employees,

the employer shall ensure that the exposure of employees to substances hazardous to health is monitored in accordance with a suitable procedure.

Regulation 10

(2)   Paragraph (1) shall not apply where the employer is able to demonstrate by another method of evaluation that the requirements of regulation 7(1) have been complied with.

(3)   The monitoring referred to in paragraph (1) shall take place –

(a)   at regular intervals; and
(b)   when any change occurs which may affect that exposure.

(4)   Where a substance or process is specified in Column 1 of Schedule 5, monitoring shall be carried out at least at the frequency specified in the corresponding entry in Column 2 of that Schedule.

(5)   The employer shall ensure that a suitable record of monitoring carried out for the purpose of this regulation is made and maintained and that that record or a suitable summary thereof is kept available –

(a)   where the record is representative of the personal exposures of identifiable employees, for at least 40 years; or
(b)   in any other case, for at least 5 years,

from the date of the last entry made in it.

(6)   Where an employee is required by regulation 11 to be under health surveillance, an individual record of any monitoring carried out in accordance with this regulation shall be made, maintained and kept in respect of that employee.

(7)   The employer shall –

(a)   on reasonable notice being given, allow an employee access to his personal monitoring record;
(b)   provide the Executive with copies of such monitoring records as the Executive may require; and
(c)   if he ceases to trade, notify the Executive forthwith in writing and make available to the Executive all monitoring records kept by him.

ACOP 10

Exposure monitoring

201   In the context of regulation 10(1), exposure monitoring means using suitable techniques to assess the extent of employees' exposure to substances hazardous to health via all routes (inhalation, ingestion and/or skin). The information gathered during exposure monitoring can help an employer assess whether the control of employees' exposure is adequate.

When exposure monitoring is required

202   Exposure monitoring is necessary if:

■   the risk assessment made under regulation 6(1) shows that an initial exploratory monitoring exercise is necessary to reach an informed and valid judgement about the risks;
■   failure or deterioration of the control measures (eg a lack of containment, or LEV not performing as intended) could result in a serious health effect, either because of the toxicity of the substance or because of the extent of potential exposure, or both;
■   measurement is required to be sure that a WEL or any self-imposed (in-house) exposure standard is not exceeded;

ACOP   **10**

- any change in the conditions affecting employees' exposure means that adequate control of exposure is no longer being maintained, eg an increase in the quantity of a substance used or from changing systems of work, or introducing new plant;
- it is needed as an additional check on the effectiveness of any control measure provided in accordance with regulation 7; this is always the case for the substances or processes specified in Schedule 5;
- the risk assessment shows it is needed to monitor for the presence of any biological agents outside the primary physical containment.

When exposure monitoring is unnecessary

203 Monitoring is not appropriate:

- if suitable techniques for sampling, analysis and quantification do not exist, or cannot be devised;
- if the employer is able to demonstrate that an alternative method of evaluation has been used to ensure that exposure is adequately controlled to comply with regulation 7. An alternative method of evaluation may include:
  - light-scattering techniques, smoke tubes, air velocity measurements;
  - use of one or more 'surrogate' measurements to assess exposure to mixtures of substances;
  - establishing whether the process is fully enclosed or is a continuous process under adequate control and any breaches of containment are monitored by fixed-site monitors with suitable warning devices.

Suitable procedures for exposure monitoring

204 Employees' exposure to substances hazardous to health can be monitored in different ways depending on the route of exposure (inhalation, skin or ingestion). The most commonly used methods are monitoring the air in the employee's breathing zone, background air monitoring, wipe sampling of the skin, biological monitoring and biological effect monitoring.

205 Air monitoring can involve personal monitoring (measuring the amount of a substance in a worker's breathing zone) to estimate individual exposures and assess control effectiveness. Results can be compared with WELs and in-house limits and used to identify task-specific exposures.

206 Air monitoring can also use suitable fixed-site air samplers (also known as static samplers) to provide an overall assessment of airborne concentrations of a substance. Fixed-site air samplers do not directly represent employee exposure. However, results can help identify:

- loss of containment and/or control;
- sources contributing to exposure;
- the extent of contaminant spread from the point of emission;
- potential exposure routes.

207 Overall, the information obtained will inform an assessment of the adequacy of control.

208 Taking wipe samples in the work area and on other surfaces, including skin, can provide useful information on the spread of substances and the potential for exposure. It is particularly useful where skin exposure and absorption is a major factor to be considered.

ACOP **10**

209 Biological monitoring is the measurement of a substance or its metabolite (substance formed when the body converts the chemical) in a biological fluid (breath, urine or blood), eg monitoring for isocyanates in urine.

210 Biological effect monitoring is used to describe the measurement of non-harmful, often reversible, biological effects in a worker following exposure, eg organophosphorus pesticide exposure can affect certain enzyme activity in the blood and this can be measured.

211 Biological monitoring and biological effect monitoring are useful to assess the degree of exposure and absorption of a substance into the body, particularly whether substances may have entered the body through the skin or via ingestion.

212 Monitoring for biological agents outside of containment to satisfy regulation 7(6)(d) may include testing:

■ the environment outside the physical means of confinement, eg a room, vessel or area around an infected human or animal;
■ the integrity of industrial process systems, eg filters, seals, or pipework joints. They may be tested by swabbing and air sampling provided that methods are suitable and validated by relevant authorities. Wherever possible, such testing should be done using harmless surrogate organisms, whose release under test conditions mimics the release of process organisms.

213 Further guidance on exposure monitoring can be found in HSE's *Monitoring strategies for toxic substances*[11] and *Biological monitoring in the workplace: A guide to its practical application to chemical exposure*.[12]

214 Suitable sampling, analytical and quantification procedures should be standardised and validated by authorities such as HSE, the British Standards Institution (BSI) or other reputable authoritative agencies such as CEN, the International Standardization Organization (ISO) and the US National Institute for Occupational Safety and Health (NIOSH). Employers should ensure that the procedures used are sufficiently sensitive for the situation being monitored and of proven effectiveness for assessing adequate control.

Who to monitor

215 Employers need to monitor those employees who are potentially at risk from exposure to substances hazardous to health where this is identified in the risk assessment carried out under regulation 6(1).

216 Where groups of employees are performing identical or similar tasks and are being exposed to similar risks to health using similar controls, sampling may be carried out on a selected number of people within the group, provided that those selected are typical of each person within the group. Care should be taken to ensure that individual work practices and human factors (eg fatigue, untrained workers) do not unduly influence the results obtained.

Frequency of monitoring

217 Monitoring carried out for the purposes of regulation 10(1) must take place at regular intervals (see regulation 10(3)(a)).

ACOP   **10**

218 In deciding the frequency of workplace exposure monitoring, the employer should take into account:

■ whether the risk assessment under regulation 6(1) recommends a frequency;

■ whether any continuous fixed-site monitoring (static monitoring) installed as part of the process control can provide information on the likely airborne exposure of employees;

■ the impact of factors such as worker behaviour, worker movements and plant failures on the systems in place to control exposure;

■ the potential health effects of exposure to the substances used in the workplace;

■ the need to assess infrequent activities, such as maintenance, during the activity concerned;

■ the need for monitoring any substances and processes listed in Schedule 5 at the minimum frequency that the Schedule specifies.

Guidance   **10**

Who should carry out exposure monitoring

219 When an employer appoints a person to carry out exposure monitoring, they should ensure that they are competent to do so (see regulation 7 of the MHSW Regulations and regulation 12(4) of COSHH). Those monitoring exposure should demonstrate:

■ appropriate training and experience in monitoring exposure;

■ familiarity with relevant monitoring standards and methods published by HSE and professional bodies;

■ adequate knowledge of occupational exposure limits and monitoring strategies;

■ adequate continuing professional development;

■ a commitment to providing sensible and proportionate advice.

220 A competent person's advice should be based on a correct assessment of the risk and take account of any established standards (eg exposure limits and principles of good practice for the control of exposure to substances hazardous to health).

221 A competent person should apply a monitoring strategy directed at the actual circumstances found in the workplace under consideration, based on a good knowledge and experience of the particular industry, process etc, and tapping into the knowledge and experience of both the management and workers at that workplace.

ACOP   **10**

Suitable exposure monitoring records

222 The information provided in exposure monitoring records should enable employers and others (eg employees, safety representatives, enforcement authorities) to understand and draw conclusions about the records' validity and the adequacy of control of employees' exposure to substances hazardous to health.

223 To be regarded as suitable, a record should contain the following details (for further advice, refer to *Monitoring strategies for toxic substances*):

■ traceability information: including employer's name and address, name of the substance monitored (including CAS number), WEL (if applicable),

ACOP   **10**

process/task description, date of monitoring, report author's name, dates of sampling and reporting;

- sampling information: including work activities during monitoring, type of sampling (breathing zone, fixed site, dermal, surface and/or biological monitoring), sample identification reference, location details, sampling duration, activity duration, references to sampling, analytical and quantification procedures;
- exposure control information: including the types of controls in place. For each type of control, the information provided should enable an assessment of the adequacy of exposure control;
- a summary: providing sufficient detail for the employer to determine whether their employees' exposure is adequately controlled to comply with the requirements of regulation 7;
- the report author's assurance: including a written confirmation, as applicable, that the report author is competent to carry out sampling and analysis, write the report and interpret the results to help the employer assess the adequacy of exposure control.

Access to exposure monitoring records

224 There are two types of records:

- a record which contains personal information (where an individual employee is identifiable);
- other types of monitoring record (where monitoring results do not identify an individual employee).

225 An employer should allow their employees to see their own individual monitoring record and confirm whether or not it demonstrates adequate exposure control. Employers may also, with the employee's consent, allow the employee's representative to see the record.

Format of the exposure monitoring report

226 The employer may keep the exposure monitoring record in any format, eg paper or electronic, and it should contain the information (see paragraph 223) necessary to assess the adequacy of control of the employee's exposure to substances hazardous to health. The assessment may include consideration of both the monitoring and health surveillance information by a responsible person (see paragraph 243–245), such as a doctor. The recorded information should be readily retrievable.

Preserving and disposing of monitoring records

227 Wherever an exposure monitoring record contains the personal exposure monitoring data of an individual employee, the record should be kept for at least 40 years from the date the record was made.

228 All other types of exposure monitoring records (eg fixed-site monitoring) should be kept for at least five years from the date the record was made.

229 Where an employer or employer's representative (eg an appointed administrator) decides that the business will cease trading, the employer should contact HSE's local office (contact details at www.hse.gov.uk/contact/maps/) and offer to provide the exposure monitoring data.

Regulation 11 Health surveillance

Regulation 11

(1)	Where it is appropriate for the protection of the health of his employees who are, or are liable to be, exposed to a substance hazardous to health, the employer shall ensure that such employees are under suitable health surveillance.

(2)	Health surveillance shall be treated as being appropriate where –

(a)	the employee is exposed to one of the substances specified in Column 1 of Schedule 6 and is engaged in a process specified in Column 2 of that Schedule, and there is a reasonable likelihood that an identifiable disease or adverse health effect will result from that exposure; or

(b)	the exposure of the employee to a substance hazardous to health is such that –
	(i)	an identifiable disease or adverse health effect may be related to the exposure;
	(ii)	there is a reasonable likelihood that the disease or effect may occur under the particular conditions of his work; and
	(iii)	there are valid techniques for detecting indications of the disease or effect,

and the technique of investigation is of low risk to the employee.

(3)	The employer shall ensure that a health record, containing particulars approved by the Executive, in respect of each of his employees to whom paragraph (1) applies, is made and maintained and that that record or a copy thereof is kept available in a suitable form for at least 40 years from the date of the last entry made in it.

(4)	The employer shall –

(a)	on reasonable notice being given, allow an employee access to his personal health record;
(b)	provide the Executive with copies of such health records as the Executive may require; and
(c)	if he ceases to trade, notify the Executive forthwith in writing and make available to the Executive all health records kept by him.

(5)	If an employee is exposed to a substance specified in Schedule 6 and is engaged in a process specified therein, the health surveillance required under paragraph (1) shall include medical surveillance under the supervision of a relevant doctor at intervals of not more than 12 months or at such shorter intervals as the relevant doctor may require.

(6)	Where an employee is subject to medical surveillance in accordance with paragraph (5) and a relevant doctor has certified by an entry in the health record of that employee that in his professional opinion that employee should not be engaged in work which exposes him to that substance or that he should only be so engaged under conditions specified in the record, the employer shall not permit the employee to be engaged in such work except in accordance with the conditions, if any, specified in the health record, unless that entry has been cancelled by a relevant doctor.

(7)	Where an employee is subject to medical surveillance in accordance with paragraph (5) and a relevant doctor has certified by an entry in his health record that medical surveillance should be continued after his exposure to that substance has ceased, the employer shall ensure that the medical surveillance of that

Regulation   **11**

employee is continued in accordance with that entry while he is employed by the employer, unless that entry has been cancelled by a relevant doctor.

(8) An employee to whom this regulation applies shall, when required by his employer and at the cost of the employer, present himself during his working hours for such health surveillance procedures as may be required for the purposes of paragraph (1) and, in the case of an employee who is subject to medical surveillance in accordance with paragraph (5), shall furnish the relevant doctor with such information concerning his health as the relevant doctor may reasonably require.

(9) Where, as a result of health surveillance, an employee is found to have an identifiable disease or adverse health effect which is considered by a relevant doctor or other occupational health professional to be the result of exposure to a substance hazardous to health the employer of that employee shall –

(a) ensure that a suitably qualified person informs the employee accordingly and provides the employee with information and advice regarding further health surveillance;
(b) review the risk assessment;
(c) review any measure taken to comply with regulation 7, taking into account any advice given by a relevant doctor, occupational health professional or by the Executive;
(d) consider assigning the employee to alternative work where there is no risk of further exposure to that substance, taking into account any advice given by a relevant doctor or occupational health professional; and
(e) provide for a review of the health of any other employee who has been similarly exposed, including a medical examination where such an examination is recommended by a relevant doctor, occupational health professional or by the Executive.

(10) Where, for the purpose of carrying out his functions under these Regulations, a relevant doctor requires to inspect any workplace or any record kept for the purposes of these Regulations, the employer shall permit him to do so.

(11) Where an employee or an employer is aggrieved by a decision recorded in the health record by a relevant doctor to suspend an employee from work which exposes him to a substance hazardous to health (or to impose conditions on such work), he may, by an application in writing to the Executive within 28 days of the date on which he was notified of the decision, apply for that decision to be reviewed in accordance with a procedure approved for the purposes of this paragraph by the Health and Safety Executive,[a] and the result of that review shall be notified to the employee and employer and entered in the health record in accordance with the approved procedure.

(a) Words substituted subject to transitional provisions as specified by SI 2008/960 Schedule 2, paragraph 11 the Legislative Reform (Health and Safety Executive) Order.

Guidance   **11**

The objectives of health surveillance

230 The objectives of health surveillance are to:

■ check the health of individual employees by detecting, as early as possible, adverse changes which may be caused by exposure to substances hazardous to health;

■ collect, keep up-to-date and use data and information for determining and evaluating hazards to health so that action can be taken to prevent more serious disease from developing;

- check control measures are working effectively by providing feedback on the accuracy of the risk assessment and the effectiveness of control measures to identify where further steps to manage risk are needed.

231 Where health surveillance shows that an employee's health is being adversely affected by their work, employers will need to take action to protect that employee's health. Before health surveillance takes place, the employer should decide:

- the criteria that should trigger action;
- the options for action, eg reassess the risk, improve controls, refer individuals for diagnosis/treatment, reassign individuals;
- how to keep health records and how to analyse and interpret the results of health surveillance.

232 Employers should also consult with the workforce and their representatives before setting up a health surveillance programme and ensure they understand why it is carried out and how they can help.

When health surveillance is appropriate

233 The risk assessment, taking account of exposure monitoring, can show where there is a need to introduce health surveillance procedures.

234 Health surveillance, including medical surveillance under the supervision of an appointed doctor, is appropriate for employees liable to be exposed to the substances and working in the processes listed in Schedule 6 if the specific conditions laid down in regulation 11(2)(a) apply. Health surveillance will also be appropriate when employees are exposed to residual risk of harm from hazardous substances, following all appropriate means of control, and when the three requirements of regulation 11(2)(b) are satisfied.

235 The judgements that employers make under regulation 11(2)(a) and (b) on the likelihood that an identifiable disease or adverse health effect will result from, or may be related to, exposure should:

- relate to the type and extent of exposure;
- be based on available knowledge of the risks to health, such as epidemiology, toxicology, exposure or extrapolation from information about similar substances or situations.

236 The aim should be to establish health surveillance procedures which are easy to perform, reproducible and reliable, preferably non-invasive and acceptable to employees. In particular, health surveillance procedures should be of low risk to workers. Where appropriate, employers should seek competent advice from occupational health professionals, such as occupational physicians, occupational nurses or occupational hygienists.

237 Examples where health surveillance is appropriate under the criteria in regulation 11(2)(b) are:

- **where there have been previous cases of work-related ill health in the workforce/place;**
- **where there is reliance on PPE, eg gloves or respirators, as an exposure control measure; eg printers wearing gloves to protect against solvents used during press cleaning, or paint sprayers using two-pack paints**

wearing respirators to prevent asthma. Even with the closest supervision there is no guarantee that PPE will be effective at all times;

■ where there is evidence of ill health in jobs within the industry; eg frequent or prolonged contact with water (termed 'wet-working') causing dermatitis in hairdressers and healthcare workers, or breathing in mists from chrome plating baths causing chrome ulcers in platers.

238 This is not a definitive or exhaustive list and there will be many other instances where health surveillance is required. Employers will need to seek information or advice on the specific health risks identified in the risk assessment, or through any topic-specific HSE guidance, trade associations or other professional sources.

Suitable health surveillance

239 As a minimum, suitable health surveillance can involve the keeping of an individual health record (see paragraphs 251–252), eg for known or suspected carcinogens (except those listed in Schedule 6).

240 In most circumstances, there is more to health surveillance than this. It will involve developing a suitable ongoing system to detect early signs of work-related ill health and check that controls are protective. This means selecting from a range of activities that may include some or all of the following:

■ a review of information on exposure, eg the results of air monitoring or biological monitoring and any related ill health;

■ a review of the risk assessment and any modifications made when necessary;

■ checks by a responsible person (see paragraphs 243–245) such as a supervisor or manager, eg for chrome ulceration or skin checks for dermatitis;

■ enquiries about symptoms, inspection or examination by a suitably qualified person, eg an occupational health professional. This may involve simple steps such as employees completing symptom questionnaires, or can include clinical examinations to assess early biological effects, eg lung function tests for asthma;

■ medical surveillance, ie a specific type of health surveillance under the supervision of an appointed doctor for the purpose of regulation 11(5). This may include clinical examination.

Health surveillance for exposure to biological agents

241 Employers should provide workers with information about the sorts of infections that are relevant to their work and the symptoms that can occur. They should train workers to exercise personal vigilance so that prompt medical attention is sought if they develop early signs of infection.

242 If the risk assessment identifies a risk of exposure to biological agents for which effective vaccines are readily available, a pre-exposure screening programme and appropriate follow-up assessments should show if employees are immune to the relevant agent (see guidance on immunisation in paragraphs 134–137). The screening records should include the dates of the employee's vaccinations and when any boosters or follow-up screenings are due.

Guidance   **11**

The person who carries out health surveillance procedures

243 The employer must ensure that those employed to conduct health surveillance are competent to do so (see regulation 7 of the MHSW Regulations).

244 For employees exposed to a substance specified in Schedule 6 and working in the related listed processes, regulation 11(5) specifies medical surveillance supervised by an HSE Appointed Doctor. The frequency of medical surveillance should be at intervals not exceeding 12 months, or at whatever shorter intervals the appointed doctor requires. The exact nature of the examination is at the doctor's direction and discretion.

245 Other health surveillance procedures may require the supervision of a registered medical practitioner. Sometimes another suitably qualified person, eg an occupational health nurse or other responsible person, can supervise the procedures. A responsible person is someone appointed by the employer who is competent (see regulation 7 of the MHSW Regulations) to carry out the relevant procedure and who is charged with reporting the conclusions of the procedure to the employer.

ACOP   **11**

Detection of an adverse health effect or identifiable disease

246 Where health surveillance shows that an employee's health is being adversely affected the employer should:

- review the risk assessment and, if necessary, modify control measures;
- check the health of employees doing similar work;
- take into account any advice received from an occupational health professional, and arrange for a suitably qualified person to explain to the employee(s) concerned:
  - the results of health surveillance;
  - any action taken to reassess the workplace controls and implement any necessary changes;
  - the arrangements for any further specialist assessment of health;
  - any arrangements which will be put in place for continuing health surveillance;
  - any arrangements to transfer the employee(s) to alternative employment within the workplace.

247 The employer should be advised by any appointed doctor or occupational health professional concerned whether:

- it is necessary to transfer the employee to other work where there is no exposure to the hazardous substance concerned;
- a medical examination of the employee concerned should be arranged and, if so, the person who should carry it out;
- all other employees who have been exposed to the substance concerned similarly to the affected employee should also be medically examined;
- additional facilities should be provided and whether any other arrangements should be made.

248 The employee or their representative should be involved before any decisions on alternative work arrangements are made.

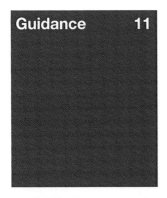

Guidance 11

Continuing health surveillance after exposure has ceased

249 In certain circumstances, eg exposure to a carcinogen, it may be appropriate for an employer to continue health surveillance of their employees (at least while they remain their employees) after exposure to a substance hazardous to health has ceased. The circumstances where this will benefit workers may be those where an adverse effect on health may be anticipated after a latent period and where it is believed that the effect can be reliably detected at a sufficiently early stage.

250 Further information on health surveillance can be found at www.hse.gov.uk/health-surveillance/.

ACOP 11

Health records

251 Employers must keep an up-to-date health record for each individual employee placed under health surveillance. It should contain at least the following:

- identifying details:
  - surname;
  - forename(s);
  - gender;
  - date of birth;
  - permanent address and postcode;
  - national insurance number;
  - date when present employment started;
  - an historical record of jobs in this employment involving exposure to identified substances requiring health surveillance;
- results of all other health surveillance procedures and the date on which, and by whom, they were carried out. The conclusions should relate only to the employee's fitness for work and will include, where appropriate:
  - a record of the decisions on an employee's fitness for continued exposure or restrictions made by the appointed doctor, or by the registered medical practitioner, occupational health nurse or other suitably qualified or responsible person;
  - whether the results require increased health surveillance.

252 The health record should not include confidential clinical data. In accordance with regulation 11(3), employers must keep these health records for at least 40 years. They may be kept in any format, eg on paper or electronically. Where records are kept electronically, employers should ensure that they have a suitable back-up system that allows access to copies of the records in the event of electronic failure.

Disposing of records when a business ceases to trade

253 When an employer or employer's representative, eg an appointed administrator, receiver or liquidator, decides that the business will cease trading, the employer must notify their HSE local office and make available to HSE all health records kept by the employer.

Access to employees' records

254 As well as allowing their employees to see their own individual health records maintained under regulation 11(3), employers may (with the employee's consent) also allow the employee's representatives to see them. Where, under regulation 11(4)(b), HSE requests copies of an employee's

ACOP   **11**

personal health records, the employer should provide the information summarised in paragraph 251.

Regulation 12 Information, instruction and training for persons who may be exposed to substances hazardous to health

Regulation   **12**

(1)   Every employer who undertakes work which is liable to expose an employee to a substance hazardous to health shall provide that employee with suitable and sufficient information, instruction and training.

(2)   Without prejudice to the generality of paragraph (1), the information, instruction and training provided under that paragraph shall include –

(a)   details of the substances hazardous to health to which the employee is liable to be exposed including –
(i)   the names of those substances and the risk which they present to health;
(ii)   any relevant workplace exposure limit or similar occupational exposure limit;
(iii)   access to any relevant safety data sheet; and
(iv)   other legislative provisions which concern the hazardous properties of those substances;
(b)   the significant findings of the risk assessment;
(c)   the appropriate precautions and actions to be taken by the employee in order to safeguard himself and other employees at the workplace;
(d)   the results of any monitoring of exposure in accordance with regulation 10 and, in particular, in the case of a substance hazardous to health for which a workplace exposure limit has been approved, the employee or his representatives shall be informed forthwith, if the results of such monitoring show that the workplace exposure limit has been exceeded;
(e)   the collective results of any health surveillance undertaken in accordance with regulation 11 in a form calculated to prevent those results from being identified as relating to a particular person; and
(f)   where employees are working with a Group 4 biological agent or material that may contain such an agent, the provision of written instructions and, if appropriate, the display of notices which outline the procedures for handling such an agent or material.

(3)   The information, instruction and training required by paragraph (1) shall be –

(a)   adapted to take account of significant changes in the type of work carried out or methods of work used by the employer; and
(b)   provided in a manner appropriate to the level, type and duration of exposure identified by the risk assessment.

(4)   Every employer shall ensure that any person (whether or not his employee) who carries out work in connection with the employer's duties under these Regulations has suitable and sufficient information, instruction and training.

(5)   Where containers and pipes for substances hazardous to health used at work are not marked in accordance with any relevant legislation listed in Schedule 7,

Regulation	12

the employer shall, without prejudice to any derogations provided for in that legislation, ensure that the contents of those containers and pipes, together with the nature of those contents and any associated hazards, are clearly identifiable.

ACOP	12

Suitable and sufficient information, instruction and training

255 In addition to the list in regulation 12(2), the information provided to employees and to other people on the premises should include, where appropriate:

- the purpose of health surveillance, the duty of employees to attend for health surveillance procedures on the appointed date and time, and arrangements for employees to have access to their individual health records (see regulation 11(4)(a) and (8));
- when to use the hygiene facilities provided and the importance of doing so in accordance with agreed procedures;
- any further relevant information resulting from a review of the assessment: why it has been done and how any changes will affect the way employees do the work in the future;
- any procedures for dealing with accidents, incidents and emergencies prepared in accordance with regulation 13.

256 Regulation 12(2)(a)(iii) allows employees access to any relevant safety data sheet. However, these sheets are not always the best or most appropriate way of providing employees with information about the risks associated with the use of hazardous substances in the workplace.

257 Employers may instead choose to distil all relevant information, including, for example, from safety data sheets, onto more readable and understandable in-house information and training documents. In doing so, employers should take great care when transcribing the information and in amplifying warnings and precautions accurately. While this is an acceptable practice, employees and their safety representatives must still be allowed access to safety data sheets relevant to the work should they want to see them.

258 The other legislative provisions referred to in regulation 12(2)(a)(iv) are those that apply directly to the hazardous substances to which employees are liable to be exposed. These may include, for example, the REACH and DSEAR Regulations for those substances which may also have a flammable, oxidising or explosive property.

259 Where workers are exposed to Hazard Group 4 biological agents, the employer must provide written instructions setting out the procedures for handling the agent.

260 If the nature of the workplace and the activity are such that workers may need instant access to this information, then it should be set out on notices displayed in the workplace.

Guidance	12

261 Employers should aim to strike a balance between providing sufficient information for an employee to carry out work safely, and providing too much information that may result in overburdening and confusing them. So where, for example, a substance is being used that is not particularly hazardous and exposure is adequately controlled, basic instructions and training may be all that is required.

Guidance 12

262 Employers have a duty under the MHSW Regulations to ensure that the information they provide is comprehensible. So they should consider the various ways of providing information, instruction and training and select those most appropriate to their own circumstances. The range of options includes: class or group tuition, individual tuition, written instructions, including leaflets and courses etc. Employers should also decide how much time is needed to provide suitable and sufficient training etc for their employees to comply fully with the requirements of the MHSW Regulations. New employees should be provided with proper induction training, which should always cover emergency and evacuation procedures.

ACOP 12

Updating information

263 Providing information, instruction and training is not a one-off exercise and should be reviewed and updated whenever significant changes are made to the type of work carried out or to the work methods used. Significant changes might include the amount of substances used or produced, new control measures, new substances brought into the workplace, or automation of certain processes. Further information and training following a review of the assessment should cover why the assessment was reviewed, any changes to the way the work is to be done and the precautions the employees should take to protect themselves and others.

Making information available to safety representatives

264 The employer must make all relevant information available to employees or their representatives in accordance with the Health and Safety (Consultation with Employees) Regulations 1996, and the Safety Representatives and Safety Committees Regulations 1977.

Instruction and training

265 The instruction and training must ensure that people at work on the premises do not put themselves or others at risk through exposure to substances hazardous to health. In particular, the instruction must be sufficient and suitable for them to know:

- how and when to use the control measures;
- the defined methods of work;
- how to use PPE, and especially RPE, eg the correct method of removing and refitting gloves and masks, and determining how long protective gloves should be worn before any liquid contamination is liable to permeate them;
- the cleaning, storage and disposal procedures they should follow, why they are required and when they are to be carried out, eg cleaning contaminated PPE with water or a vacuum fitted with a HEPA filter, and not with an airline, and the risks of using contaminated PPE;
- the procedures to be followed in an emergency.

266 Training should include elements of theory as well as practice. Training in the use and application of control measures and PPE should take account of recommendations and instructions supplied by the manufacturer.

Guidance 12

Records of training

267 Employers may find it helpful to keep a record of the training given to individual employees or specific groups of named employees. The records may

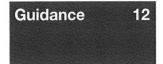

Guidance   **12**

provide a useful checklist for ensuring that employees receive the necessary training etc at the appropriate time. The records may also help to resolve any disputes that arise about whether the employer has provided a particular employee with a specific aspect of information, instruction and training.

ACOP   **12**

People carrying out work on behalf of the employer

268 The employer must ensure that the person, or people, to whom any work is delegated is competent to do it and this may mean having to use the services of consultants and outside experts. If this becomes necessary, the employer will still need to ensure that the people involved receive sufficient information about the particular circumstances of the work, including the hazardous substances used or produced and their hazardous properties.

269 People carrying out the work required under regulations 6, 7, 9, 10, 11 and 13 of COSHH should have adequate knowledge, training and expertise in the assessment, evaluation and control of risks arising from exposure to substances hazardous to health.

Guidance   **12**

270 Employers have duties under regulation 7 of the MHSW Regulations to appoint one or more competent people to help them carry out the measures needed to comply with health and safety legislation. The MHSW Regulations also require that, where the employer has an employee with the necessary competence to provide the required assistance, the employer should appoint the employee to do the work in preference to someone who is not in their employment. Wherever practicable, therefore, suitable employees should be encouraged to have appropriate training, and to gain the knowledge and expertise that will give them the competence to help their employers comply with health and safety requirements.

271 For more complex situations expert advice may be appropriate. HSE does not define or approve standards of competence, but those seeking expert advice may wish to consult the Occupational Safety and Health Consultants' Register (www.hse.gov.uk/oshcr/).

Identifying the contents of containers and pipes

272 Regulation 12(5) is intended to cover those circumstances where there is no other legal requirement for employers to identify the hazardous contents of containers and pipes. The legal requirements which implement European directives are listed in Schedule 7.

273 Many containers will therefore already be adequately marked with their contents because of supply requirements. Similarly, pipework is often marked in accordance with BS 1710:1984 *Specification for identification of pipelines and services*,[13] or equivalent 'in-house' standards. However, there may be containers and pipes whose contents are not individually marked because it is not practicable to do so, eg the pipework at large petrochemical complexes whose content may change frequently during the course of a process or operation.

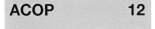

ACOP   **12**

274 In these and similar circumstances to which regulation 12(5) applies, employers should ensure that they have suitable procedures in place to identify the hazardous contents of containers and pipes at any given time. The identification process may involve reference to working procedures, to operating instructions or to computer models which identify individual plant components by name or number.

ACOP   **12**

275 Complex plant or batch processing may require components to be used for different hazardous substances over short periods of time and, in these circumstances, employees will need to be familiar with the plant operations and the sources of information available to them. Whichever identification procedure employers adopt, they must ensure that employees and safety representatives are familiar with any plans, characters, signs, symbols, codes etc that the identification system or procedures use.

276 It is particularly important for repair or maintenance work involving the opening of vessels or breaking into pipework to be carried out under the control of a 'permit-to-work' system. For this work, identifying the hazardous substances in a container or pipe is one essential element of the risk assessment that must be carried out before the work starts. For employers to carry out suitable and sufficient assessments of the work in these circumstances, they must have a system in place which identifies:

- the name(s) of the hazardous substances which containers and pipes contain or contained;
- the form the hazardous substance(s) takes, eg liquid, semi-liquid, sludge, powder, waste mixed with other identified material;
- the hazards the substance(s) could pose if employees were exposed to the contents, eg irritation or burns to the skin from spilt liquids.

Regulation 13 Arrangements to deal with accidents, incidents and emergencies

Regulation   **13**

(1)   Subject to paragraph (4) and without prejudice to the relevant provisions of the Management of Health and Safety at Work Regulations 1999, in order to protect the health of his employees from an accident, incident or emergency related to the presence of a substance hazardous to health at the workplace, the employer shall ensure that –

(a)   procedures, including the provision of appropriate first-aid facilities and relevant safety drills (which shall be tested at regular intervals), have been prepared which can be put into effect when such an event occurs;

(b)   information on emergency arrangements, including –

(i)   details of relevant work hazards and hazard identification arrangements; and

(ii)   specific hazards likely to arise at the time of an accident, incident or emergency, is available; and

(c)   suitable warning and other communication systems are established to enable an appropriate response, including remedial actions and rescue operations, to be made immediately when such an event occurs.

(2)   The employer shall ensure that information on the procedures and systems required by paragraph (1)(a) and (c) and the information required by paragraph (1)(b) is –

(a)   made available to relevant accident and emergency services to enable those services, whether internal or external to the workplace, to prepare their own response procedures and precautionary measures; and

(b)   displayed at the workplace, if this is appropriate.

(3)   Subject to paragraph (4), in the event of an accident, incident or emergency related to the presence of a substance hazardous to health at the

Regulation 13

workplace, the employer shall ensure that –

(a) immediate steps are taken to –
  (i) mitigate the effects of the event;
  (ii) restore the situation to normal; and
  (iii) inform those of his employees who may be affected;
(b) only those persons who are essential for the carrying out of repairs and other necessary work are permitted in the affected area and they are provided with –
  (i) appropriate personal protective equipment; and
  (ii) any necessary specialised safety equipment and plant, which shall be used until the situation is restored to normal; and
(c) in the case of an incident or accident which has or may have resulted in the release of a biological agent which could cause severe human disease, as soon as practicable thereafter his employees or their representatives are informed of –
  (i) the causes of that incident or accident; and
  (ii) the measures taken or to be taken to rectify the situation.

(4) Paragraph (1) and, provided the substance hazardous to health is not a carcinogen, mutagen or biological agent, paragraph (3) shall not apply where –

(a) the results of the risk assessment show that, because of the quantity of each substance hazardous to health present at the workplace, there is only a slight risk to the health of employees; and
(b) the measures taken by the employer to comply with the duty under regulation 7(1) are sufficient to control that risk.

(5) An employee shall report forthwith, to his employer or to any other employee of that employer with specific responsibility for the health and safety of his fellow employees, any accident or incident which has or may have resulted in the release of a biological agent which could cause severe human disease.

Guidance 13

General

277 The requirements contained in this regulation are in addition to those contained in regulation 8 of the MHSW Regulations. Those Regulations impose a number of general duties on all employers to establish procedures to deal with situations involving serious and imminent danger.

Emergency procedures relating to substances hazardous to health

278 For the purpose of regulation 13, an accident, incident or emergency is any event which causes, or threatens to cause, any employee to be exposed to one or more hazardous substances on a scale, or to an extent, well beyond that associated with normal day-to-day activity. Examples of this sort of event include:

■ any process fire which could give rise to a serious risk to health;
■ any serious spillage or flood of a corrosive agent liable to make contact with employees' skin;
■ any failure to contain biological, carcinogenic, mutagenic or sensitising agents;
■ any acute process failure that could lead to a sudden release of chemicals, eg an exothermic reaction that results in emission of toxic fumes;
■ any threatened significant exposure over a WEL, eg where the exposure is clearly the result of an unusual, sudden and serious failure of LEV or other controls.

Guidance   13

279 Whether an uncontrolled release or a leak or spillage of a substance hazardous to health should be regarded as an incident for the purpose of regulation 13 will depend on the scale of the release and the substance concerned and its properties. Employers should use their judgement to decide whether the incident can be dealt with under the prevention and control requirements of regulation 7, or whether it is necessary to invoke emergency arrangements.

280 The response to an emergency should also be proportionate to the risk. So, employers should also decide what proportionate action is needed to deal with the situation, eg not all incidents will automatically require the evacuation of the workplace.

281 In the context of regulation 13(1)(a), 'relevant safety drills' can be any one or more of a number of emergency procedures unique to the circumstances of the particular workplace and incident. It can mean, for example:

- a complete evacuation of the premises;
- the action taken by certain personnel in the event of an emergency, such as isolating plant or equipment;
- the steps taken by nominated personnel to help disabled staff leave the building;
- a general fire drill.

ACOP   13

282 Employers need not extend the scope of their general emergency procedures drawn up under regulation 8 of the MHSW Regulations if they are satisfied that:

- the quantity and type of hazardous substance(s) at the workplace would either individually or cumulatively create no more than a slight risk because they have a low toxic effect;
- existing control measures and emergency arrangements are sufficient to contain and control any risk to health that the substances might pose during an emergency, and that they are capable of quickly restoring the situation to normal.

283 If the conditions described above do not apply, employers must extend their emergency procedures as required by regulation 13 and ensure that they are capable of limiting the extent of any risks to health of employees and, SFARP, the health of anyone else likely to be affected by the incident, eg people living in the neighbourhood.

284 Employers may integrate the emergency procedures they draw up under the MHSW Regulations and COSHH with those required by other legislation which applies to their workplace, eg DSEAR, or the Control of Major Accident Hazard Regulations 1999 (COMAH). Emergency arrangements drawn up under COMAH may already implement most of the requirements of regulation 13 of COSHH. Employers should ensure that emergency arrangements drawn up under COSHH do not conflict with requirements drawn up under other regulations.

285 To deal with situations which could present significantly greater risks, employers should extend their emergency procedures to include details of the following:

- *the identity of hazardous substances* present at the workplace, where they are stored, used, processed or produced, and an estimate of the amount in the workplace on an average day;

ACOP 13
- *the foreseeable types of accidents, incidents or emergencies* which might occur, and the hazards they could present. Consider where such incidents might occur, what effect they might have, the other areas that might be affected by the incident spreading, and any possible repercussions;
- *the special arrangements to deal with an emergency situation* not covered by the general procedures, and the steps to be taken to mitigate the effects;
- *the safety equipment and PPE* to be used in the event of an accident, incident or emergency, where it is stored, and who is authorised to use it;
- *first-aid facilities* sufficient to deal with an incident until the emergency services arrive, where the facilities are located and stored, and the likely effects on the workforce of the accident, incident or emergency;
- *the role, responsibilities and authority* of the people nominated to manage the accident, incident or emergency, and the individuals with specific duties in the event of an incident;
- *procedures for employees* to follow and details of who should know these, how they should respond to an incident, what action they should take, and the roles of the people who have been assigned specific responsibilities;
- *procedures for clearing up* and safely disposing of any substances hazardous to health that are damaged or 'contaminated' during the incident;
- *regular safety drills*. The frequency of practising emergency procedures will depend on the complexity of the layout of the workplace, the activities carried out, the level of risk, the size of the workforce, the amount of substances involved, and the success of each test;
- *the special needs* of any disabled employees, eg assigning other employees to help them leave the workplace in an emergency.

Incidents involving carcinogens, mutagens and sensitisers

286 If an incident results in the uncontrolled release of a carcinogen, mutagen or sensitiser into the workplace, the equipment the employer provides under regulation 13(3)(b) must always include suitable PPE, including RPE, which can provide adequate control of exposure to the carcinogenic or mutagenic substance concerned.

Incidents or accidents involving a biological agent

287 The control measures required by regulation 7 should provide adequate safe systems of work for dealing with most spillages and incidents involving biological agents, such as cleaning up, disinfection and disposal of contaminated waste, incident recording and referral for medical advice, if required.

288 In deliberate work with biological agents, there are circumstances in which an accident or incident involving the release of an agent could cause severe disease for the worker (Hazard Group 3 and 4 biological agents), and the potential to infect others is such that an accident or emergency response procedure will be needed.

289 The risk assessment should determine when this is required and should be proportionate to the risk. The employer will need to identify whether employees would need to have instant access to emergency procedures to help contain an accidental release (see paragraph 302).

ACOP   **13**

290 Employees must immediately report any release of a biological agent in Hazard Group 3 or 4. Employees who may need to report such incidents should be provided with:

- information on readily foreseeable incidents that could occur;
- the procedures for dealing with accidents, incidents and emergencies;
- the name of the person or people to whom accidents should be reported and the follow-up actions that the employer will take, including arrangements for accident investigation, referral for medical advice and taking action to prevent a recurrence.

Suitable warning and communication systems

291 Employers must provide suitable communication systems for warning employees who are liable to be affected by an accident, incident or emergency involving substances hazardous to health. The communication system the employer provides should be proportionate to the size of the workplace and workforce, the quantity of substances hazardous to health in the workplace, and the level and type of risk the substances present.

292 The employer may consider it appropriate to provide warning signals for different purposes, ie one type of alarm to warn employees of the need to be prepared to evacuate because an incident is declared, and another to signal the immediate need to evacuate the premises. Suitable warning systems might include a continuous or intermittent ringing bell, whistle or hooter, warning lights or an intercom or public address system.

293 Employers must ensure that all warning systems can be heard and/or seen in all parts of the premises, and in particular by employees who may work in noisier areas. Employers should also ensure that they take account of the special needs of disabled employees.

Reviewing the emergency procedures

294 The employer should review, update and replace the emergency procedures in the light of changing circumstances, eg a significant increase in the use of a particularly hazardous substance, changes in the workplace activities involving the use of a new substance hazardous to health etc.

Making procedures available to the emergency services

295 Employers should ensure that copies of their emergency arrangements and procedures are made available to the relevant internal and external accident and emergency services.

Internal emergency services

296 Internal services include those people assigned specific duties in the event of an accident, incident or emergency. Employers should arrange for all the people concerned to be provided with their own copy of the emergency procedures. Copies may be provided on paper or electronically.

External emergency services

297 Employers who need to extend their emergency procedures to cover situations involving substances hazardous to health should consider whether

ACOP   **13**

it is necessary to make all branches of the emergency service aware of their arrangements to deal with accidents and incidents.

Guidance   **13**

298 The employer's emergency procedures, including details of the substances hazardous to health present at the workplace, will help the fire service to prepare its own response procedures and precautionary measures if an emergency is declared at the employer's workplace. These measures will ensure that the fire service deals with any declared incident effectively, and especially those likely to occur outside normal working hours, in a way that presents the minimum risk to their own staff.

299 If an incident could have serious repercussions on the environment, the employer should consider whether to make a copy of the business's emergency procedures available to the relevant authority.

ACOP   **13**

300 A record of the procedures may be kept in writing or recorded by other means, eg electronically. It must be kept readily accessible and retrievable for examination at any reasonable time, eg by a safety representative, inspector etc.

Displaying emergency procedures

301 Where it is appropriate to do so, employers should display the emergency procedures in a prominent position in the workplace for employees to read, eg on employee noticeboards. It will be appropriate, for example, where:

- the company is fairly small and employees are encouraged to consult their noticeboard(s) frequently for information about the business and its activities;
- the emergency procedures are reasonably short and simple and can comfortably fit on the noticeboard.

Employer's actions during an emergency

302 The specific actions an employer must take if an accident, incident or emergency occurs are set out in regulation 13(3). The employer must ensure that those employees given the task of identifying the source of the release and making repairs wear appropriate PPE, including, where necessary, suitable RPE and protective clothing with which they have been provided until the situation is restored to normal.

303 As well as telling employees the cause of the incident and the measures taken, or to be taken, to resolve it, the employer should also ensure that:

- any important lessons learned from it are passed onto the employees and/or their appointed safety representatives;
- the information is used in any subsequent review of the risk assessment for the process or activity concerned.

Guidance   **13**

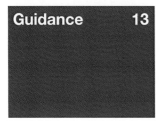

304 When an incident is declared, employers also have a duty to tell, and if necessary evacuate, other people who are present in the workplace and who may be affected by it. This includes visitors, employees of another employer etc. Employers whose activities involve the presence of certain listed dangerous substances at the workplace also have a duty under COMAH to take all measures necessary to prevent major accidents and to limit their consequences to people and the environment.

Regulation 14 Provisions relating to certain fumigations

Regulation   14

(1)   This regulation shall apply to fumigations in which the fumigant used or intended to be used is hydrogen cyanide, phosphine or methyl bromide, except that paragraph (2) shall not apply to fumigations using the fumigant specified in Column 1 of Schedule 8 when the nature of the fumigation is that specified in the corresponding entry in Column 2 of that Schedule.

(2)   An employer shall not undertake fumigation to which this regulation applies unless he has –

(a)   notified the persons specified in Part I of Schedule 9 of his intention to undertake the fumigation; and
(b)   provided to those persons the information specified in Part II of that Schedule,

at least 24 hours in advance, or such shorter time in advance as the persons required to be notified may agree.

(3)   An employer who undertakes a fumigation to which this regulation applies shall ensure that, before the fumigant is released, suitable warning notices have been affixed at all points of reasonable access to the premises or to those parts of the premises in which the fumigation is to be carried out and that after the fumigation has been completed, and the premises are safe to enter, those warning notices are removed.

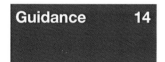

305   Schedule 8 to the Regulations lists a number of fumigations exempted from the notification requirements of regulation 14. For all three specified gases, these exemptions include fumigations carried out for research and also fumigation in fumigation chambers.

Regulation 15 Exemption certificates

Regulation   15

(1)   Subject to paragraph (2) the Executive may, by a certificate in writing, exempt any person or class of persons or any substance or class of substances from all or any of the requirements or prohibitions imposed by regulations 4 (to the extent permitted by article 9 of Council Directive 98/24/EC), 8, 9, 11(8), (10) and (11) and 14 of these Regulations and any such exemption may be granted subject to conditions and to a limit of time and may be revoked by a certificate in writing at any time.

(2)   The Executive shall not grant any such exemption unless having regard to the circumstances of the case and, in particular, to –

(a)   the conditions, if any, which it proposes to attach to the exemption; and
(b)   any requirements imposed by or under any enactments which apply to the case,

it is satisfied that the health and safety of persons who are likely to be affected by the exemption will not be prejudiced in consequence of it.

Regulation 16 Exemptions relating to the Ministry of Defence etc

Regulation 16

(1) In this regulation –

(a) "Her Majesty's Forces" means any of the naval, military or air forces of the Crown, whether raised inside or outside the United Kingdom and whether any such force is a regular, auxiliary or reserve force, and includes any civilian employed by those forces;

(b) "visiting force" has the same meaning as it does for the purposes of any provision of Part I of the Visiting Forces Act 1952; and

(c) "headquarters" means a headquarters for the time being specified in Schedule 2 to the Visiting Forces and International Headquarters (Application of Law) Order 1999.

(2) The Secretary of State for Defence may, in the interests of national security, by a certificate in writing exempt –

(a) any of Her Majesty's Forces;

(b) any visiting force;

(c) members of a visiting force working in or attached to a headquarters; or

(d) any person engaged in work involving substances hazardous to health, if that person is under the direct supervision of a representative of the Secretary of State for Defence,

from all or any of the requirements or prohibitions imposed by these Regulations and any such exemption may be granted subject to conditions and to a limit of time and may be revoked at any time by a certificate in writing, except that, where any such exemption is granted, suitable arrangements shall be made for the assessment of the health risk created by the work involving substances hazardous to health and for adequately controlling the exposure to those substances of persons to whom the exemption relates.

(3) Regulation 11(11) shall not apply in relation to –

(a) any visiting force; or

(b) members of a visiting force working in or attached to a headquarters.

Guidance 16

306 The Secretary of State for Defence has the power to exempt only in the interests of national security, ie when the state is under threat or otherwise facing an emergency. Exemptions, if needed, should be in writing and would be issued, after consultation with HSE, for specific activities and for a limited period only. When an exemption is granted, suitable arrangements should still be made to assess the risk to health from the work and to adequately control the exposure.

307 A person under the direct supervision of a representative of the Secretary of State for Defence is an employee of the Ministry of Defence (MOD) or a member of Her Majesty's Forces. It also includes certain people employed on MOD premises. For example, this could include people on a labour-only contract, but whether or not there is direct supervision will depend on the type of contract. People employed on the premises of defence contractors are most unlikely to be under such direct supervision. For example, MOD liaison staff at a defence contractor's premises do not normally exercise direct supervision.

Regulation 16A Modifications relating to the Office of Rail Regulation[a]

Regulation	16A

(1)   In so far as these Regulations apply to, or in connection with, any activities in relation to which the Office of Rail Regulation is made the enforcing authority by regulation 3(1) of the Health and Safety (Enforcing Authority for Railways and Other Guided Transport Systems) Regulations 2006, they shall have effect as if any reference to the Executive in the provisions specified in paragraph (2) were a reference to the Office of Rail Regulation.

(2)   The provisions referred to in paragraph (1) are as follows –

(a)   regulation 10(7)(b) (monitoring exposure at the workplace);
(b)   regulation 11(4)(b) (health surveillance); and
(c)   regulation 18 (revocation and savings).

(a)   Added by the Health and Safety (Enforcing Authority for Railways and Other Guided Transport Systems) Regulations 2006/557 Schedule 1, paragraph 11 (April 1, 2006).

Regulation 17 Extension outside Great Britain

Regulation	17

(1)   Subject to paragraph (2), these Regulations shall apply to and in relation to any activity outside Great Britain to which sections 1 to 59 and 80 to 82 of the 1974 Act apply by virtue of the Health and Safety at Work etc Act 1974 (Application outside Great Britain) Order 2001 as those provisions apply within Great Britain.

(2)   These Regulations shall not extend to Northern Ireland except insofar as they relate to imports of substances and articles referred to in regulation 4(2) into the United Kingdom.

308 This regulation applies COSHH to certain offshore activities, as provided for by the HSW Act (Application outside Great Britain) Order 2001 (as amended). These include, for example, offshore installations, wells, pipelines and pipeline works, and connected activities within the territorial waters of Great Britain or in designated areas of the United Kingdom Continental Shelf, plus certain other activities within territorial waters.

Regulation 18 Revocation and savings

Regulation	18

(1)   The Control of Substances Hazardous to Health Regulations 1999 are revoked.

(2)   Any record or register required to be kept under the Regulations revoked by paragraph (1) shall, notwithstanding that revocation, be kept in the same manner and for the same period as specified in those Regulations as if these Regulations had not been made, except that the Executive may approve the keeping of records at a place or in a form other than at the place where, or in the form in which, records were required to be kept under the Regulations so revoked.

Regulation 19 Extension of meaning of "work"

Regulation	19

For the purposes of Part I of the 1974 Act the meaning of "work" shall be extended to include any activity involving the consignment, storage or use of a Group 2, 3 or 4 biological agent and the meaning of "at work" shall be extended accordingly, and in that connection the references to employer in paragraphs 5 and 6 of Schedule 3 include references to any persons carrying out such an activity.

Regulation 20 Modification of section 3(2) of the 1974 Act

Regulation	20

Section 3(2) of the 1974 Act shall be modified in relation to an activity involving the consignment, storage or use of any of the biological agents referred to in regulation 19 so as to have effect as if the reference therein to a self-employed person is a reference to any person who is not an employer or an employee and the reference therein to his undertaking includes a reference to such an activity.

Regulation 21 Defence

Regulation	21

Subject to regulation 21 of the Management of Health and Safety at Work Regulations 1999, in any proceedings for an offence consisting of a contravention of these Regulations it shall be a defence for any person to prove that he took all reasonable precautions and exercised all due diligence to avoid the commission of that offence.

Schedule 1 Other substances and processes to which the definition of "carcinogen" relates

Schedule 1

Regulation 2(1)
Aflatoxins.

Arsenic.

Auramine manufacture.

Calcining, sintering or smelting of nickel copper matte or acid leaching or electrorefining of roasted matte.

Coal soots, coal tar, pitch and coal tar fumes.

Hardwood dusts.

Isopropyl alcohol manufacture (strong acid process).

Leather dust in boot and shoe manufacture, arising during preparation and finishing.

Magenta manufacture.

Mustard gas (ß, ß' -dichlorodiethyl sulphide).

Rubber manufacturing and processing giving rise to rubber process dust and rubber fume.

Used engine oils.

The following polychlorodibenzodioxins:

2,3,7,8-TCDD

1,2,3,7,8-PeCDD

1,2,3,4,7,8-HxCDD

1,2,3,6,7,8-HxCDD

1,2,3,7,8,9-HxCDD

1,2,3,4,6,7,8-HpCDD

OCDD,

The following polychlorodibenzofurans:

Schedule 1	*2,3,7,8-TCDF*
	2,3,4,7,8-PeCDF
	1,2,3,7,8-PeCDF
	1,2,3,4,7,8-HxCDF
	1,2,3,7,8,9-HxCDF
	1,2,3,6,7,8-HxCDF
	2,3,4,6,7,8-HxCDF
	1,2,3,4,6,7,8-HpCDF
	1,2,3,4,7,8,9-HpCDF
	OCDF

Where T=tetra, Pe=penta, Hx=hexa, Hp=hepta and O=octa.

Schedule 2 Prohibition of certain substances hazardous to health for certain purposes

Schedule 2

Regulation 4(1)

Column 1		Column 2
Description of substance		*Purpose for which the substance is prohibited*
1	2-naphthylamine; benzidine;	*Manufacture and use for all purposes including any manufacturing process in which a substance described in Column 1 of this item is formed.*
	4-aminodiphenyl;	
	4-nitrodiphenyl; their salts and any substance containing any of those compounds, in a total concentration equal to or greater than 0.1 per cent by mass.	
2	Sand or other substance containing free silica.	*Use as an abrasive for blasting articles in any blasting apparatus.*
3	A substance (a) containing compounds of silicon calculated as silica to the extent of more than 3 per cent by weight of dry material, other than natural sand, zirconium silicate (zircon), calcined china clay, calcined aluminous fireclay, sillimanite, calcined or fused alumina, olivine; or (b) composed of or containing dust or other matter deposited from a fettling or blasting process.	*Use as a parting material in connection with the making of metal castings.*
4	Carbon disulphide.	*Use in the cold-cure process of vulcanising in the proofing of cloth with rubber.*

Schedule 2	Column 1	Column 2
	Description of substance	**Purpose for which the substance is prohibited**
	5 Oils other than white oil, or oil of entirely animal or vegetable origin or entirely of mixed animal and vegetable origin.	Use for oiling the spindles of self-acting mules.
	6 Ground or powdered flint or quartz other than natural sand.	Use in relation to the manufacture or decoration of pottery for the following purposes: (a) the placing of ware for the biscuit fire; (b) the polishing of ware; (c) as the ingredient of a wash for saggars, trucks, bats, cranks, or other articles used in supporting ware during firing; and (d) as dusting or supporting powder in potters' shops.

	7 Ground or powdered flint or quartz other than:
	(a) natural sand; or
	(b) ground or powdered flint or quartz
	which forms parts of a slop or paste.
		Use in relation to the manufacture or decoration of pottery for any purpose except:
		(a) use in a separate room or building for:
		  (i) the manufacture of powdered flint or quartz; or
		  (ii) the making of frits or glazes or the making of colours or coloured slips for the decoration of pottery;
		(b) use for the incorporation of the substance into the body of ware in an enclosure in which no person is employed and which is constructed and ventilated to prevent the escape of dust.

	8 Dust or powder of a refractory material containing not less than 80 per cent of silica other than natural sand.	Use for sprinkling the moulds of silica bricks, namely bricks or other articles composed of refractory material and containing not less than 80 per cent of silica.
	9 White phosphorus.	Use in the manufacture of matches.

Schedule 2		

Column 1		Column 2
Description of substance		**Purpose for which the substance is prohibited**
10	Hydrogen cyanide.	Use in fumigation except when: (a) released from an inert material in which hydrogen cyanide is absorbed; (b) generated from a gassing powder; or (c) applied from a cylinder through suitable piping and applicators other than for fumigation in the open air to control or kill mammal pests.
[11–13	Entries repealed by REACH Enforcement Regulations 2008/2852 Schedule 10(2), paragraph 1 (June 1, 2009)]	

In this Schedule –

"aerosol dispenser" means an article which consists of a non-reusable receptacle containing a gas compressed, liquefied or dissolved under pressure, with or without liquid, paste or powder and fitted with a release device allowing the contents to be ejected as solid or liquid particles in suspension in a gas, as a foam, paste or powder or in a liquid state;

"blasting apparatus" means apparatus for cleaning, smoothing, roughening or removing of part of the surface of any article by the use as an abrasive of a jet of sand, metal shot or grit or other material propelled by a blast of compressed air or steam or by a wheel;

"CAS No" is the number assigned to a substance by the Chemical Abstract Service;

"cosmetic product" has the meaning assigned to it in Article 2 of Regulation (EC) No 1223/2009 of the European Parliament and of the Council on cosmetic products (recast) as amended from time to time[a] (including any aerosol dispenser containing a cosmetic product);

"gassing powder" means a chemical compound in powder form which reacts with atmospheric moisture to generate hydrogen cyanide;

"medicinal product" means a substance or preparation which is –

(a) intended for use as a medicinal product within the meaning of section 130 of the Medicines Act 1968; or

(b) a substance or preparation specified in an order made under section 104 or 105 of the Medicines Act 1968 which is for the time being in force and which directs that specified provisions of that Act shall have effect in relation to that substance or preparation as such provisions have effect in relation to medicinal products within the meaning of that Act;

Schedule 2

"use as a parting material" means the application of the material to the surface or parts of the surface of a pattern or of a mould so as to facilitate the separation of the pattern from the mould or the separation of parts of the mould;

"white oil" means a refined mineral oil conforming to a specification approved by the Executive and certified by its manufacturer as so conforming.

(a)   Words substituted by the Cosmetic Products Enforcement Regulations 2013/1478 Schedule 5, paragraph 13 (July 11, 2013).

Schedule 2A Principles of good practice for the control of exposure to substances hazardous to health

Schedule 2A

Regulation 7(7)

(a) Design and operate processes and activities to minimise emission, release and spread of substances hazardous to health.

(b) Take into account all relevant routes of exposure – inhalation, skin absorption and ingestion – when developing control measures.

(c) Control exposure by measures that are proportionate to the health risk.

(d) Choose the most effective and reliable control options which minimise the escape and spread of substances hazardous to health.

(e) Where adequate control of exposure cannot be achieved by other means, provide, in combination with other control measures, suitable personal protective equipment.

(f) Check and review regularly all elements of control measures for their continuing effectiveness.

(g) Inform and train all employees on the hazards and risks from the substances with which they work and the use of control measures developed to minimise the risks.

(h) Ensure that the introduction of control measures does not increase the overall risk to health and safety.

Guidance Schedule 2A

309 Further information on the principles of good practice for the control of hazardous substances can be found in paragraphs 99–119, and also on HSE's COSHH webpages at www.hse.gov.uk/coshh/.

Schedule 3 Additional provisions relating to work with biological agents

Schedule	3

Regulation 7(10)

PART I Provisions of general application to biological agents

1   Interpretation

In this Schedule "diagnostic service" means any activity undertaken solely with the intention of analysing specimens or samples from a human patient or animal in which a biological agent is or is suspected of being present for purposes relating to the assessment of the clinical progress, or assistance in the clinical management, of that patient or animal, and "diagnosis" shall be construed accordingly.

2   Classification of biological agents

(1)   Where a biological agent does not have an approved classification, the employer shall provisionally classify that agent in accordance with sub-paragraph (2), having regard to the nature of the agent and the properties of which he may reasonably be expected to be aware.

(2)   When provisionally classifying a biological agent the employer shall assign that agent to one of the following Groups according to its level of risk of infection and, if in doubt as to which of two alternative Groups is the most appropriate, he shall assign it to the higher of the two –

(a)   Group 1 – unlikely to cause human disease;
(b)   Group 2 – can cause human disease and may be a hazard to employees; it is unlikely to spread to the community and there is usually effective prophylaxis or treatment available;
(c)   Group 3 – can cause severe human disease and may be a serious hazard to employees; it may spread to the community, but there is usually effective prophylaxis or treatment available;
(d)   Group 4 – causes severe human disease and is a serious hazard to employees; it is likely to spread to the community and there is usually no effective prophylaxis or treatment available.

(3)   Where an employer is using a biological agent which has an approved classification and the risk of infection for that particular agent is different to that expected, the employer shall reclassify the agent in consultation with the Executive as if performing a provisional classification under sub-paragraph (2).

3   Special control measures for laboratories, animal rooms and industrial processes

(1)   Every employer who is engaged in any of the activities specified in sub-paragraph (3) shall ensure that measures taken to control adequately the exposure of his employees to biological agents include, in particular, the most suitable

Schedule   3

combination of containment measures from those listed in Parts II and III of this Schedule as appropriate, taking into account –

(a)   the nature of the activity specified in sub-paragraph (3);
(b)   the minimum containment level specified in sub-paragraph (4);
(c)   the risk assessment; and
(d)   the nature of the biological agent concerned.

(2)   An employer who is engaged in –

(a)   any of the activities specified in sub-paragraph (3)(a) or (b) shall select measures from Part II of this Schedule;
(b)   the activity specified in sub-paragraph (3)(c) shall select measures from Part III of this Schedule and, subject to sub-paragraph (4), when making that selection he may combine measures from different containment levels on the basis of a risk assessment related to any particular process or part of a process.

(3)   The activities referred to in sub-paragraph (1) are –

(a)   research, development, teaching or diagnostic work in laboratories which involves working with a Group 2, Group 3 or Group 4 biological agent or material containing such an agent;
(b)   working with animals which have been deliberately infected with a Group 2, Group 3 or Group 4 biological agent or which are, or are suspected of being, naturally infected with such an agent; and
(c)   industrial processes which involve working with a Group 2, Group 3 or Group 4 biological agent.

(4)   Subject to sub-paragraph (5), the minimum containment level referred to in sub-paragraph (1) shall be –

(a)   level 2 for activities which involve working with a Group 2 biological agent;
(b)   level 3 for activities which involve working with a Group 3 biological agent;
(c)   level 4 for activities which involve working with a Group 4 biological agent;
(d)   level 2 for laboratories which do not intentionally propagate, concentrate or otherwise increase the risk of exposure to a biological agent but work with materials in respect of which it is unlikely that a Group 3 or Group 4 biological agent is present;
(e)   level 3 or 4, where appropriate, for laboratories which do not intentionally propagate, concentrate or otherwise increase the risk of exposure to a Group 3 or Group 4 biological agent but where the employer knows, or it is likely, that such a containment level is necessary; and
(f)   level 3 for activities where it has not been possible to carry out a conclusive assessment but where there is concern that the activity might involve a serious health risk for employees.

(5)   The Health and Safety Executive[a] may approve guidelines specifying the minimum containment measures which are to apply in any particular case.

(6)   The Health and Safety Executive[a] shall not approve any guidelines under paragraph (5) unless it is satisfied that the health of any person who is likely to be affected by the use of those guidelines will not be prejudiced.

Schedule 3

(a) Words substituted subject to transitional provisions as specified by SI 2008/960 Schedule 2, paragraph 11 the Legislative Reform (Health and Safety Executive) Order.

4 List of employees exposed to certain biological agents

(1) Subject to sub-paragraph (2), every employer shall keep a list of employees exposed to a Group 3 or Group 4 biological agent, indicating the type of work done and, where known, the biological agent to which they have been exposed, and records of exposures, accidents and incidents, as appropriate.

(2) Sub-paragraph (1) shall not apply where the results of the risk assessment indicate that –

(a) the activity does not involve a deliberate intention to work with or use that biological agent; and

(b) there is no significant risk to the health of employees associated with that biological agent.

(3) The employer shall ensure that the list or a copy thereof is kept available in a suitable form for at least 40 years from the date of the last entry made in it.

(4) The relevant doctor referred to in regulation 11, and any employee of that employer with specific responsibility for the health and safety of his fellow employees, shall have access to the list.

(5) Each employee shall have access to the information on the list which relates to him personally.

5 Notification of the use of biological agents

(1) Subject to sub-paragraphs (7) and (8), an employer shall not use for the first time one or more biological agents in Group 2, 3 or 4 at particular premises for any of the activities listed in paragraph 3(3) unless he has –

(a) notified the Executive in writing of his intention to do so at least 20 working days in advance, or such shorter period as the Executive may allow;

(b) furnished with that notification the particulars specified in sub-paragraph (5); and

(c) received the acknowledgement required by sub-paragraph (4).

(2) Subject to sub-paragraphs (7) and (9), an employer shall not use a biological agent which is specified in Part V of this Schedule, except where the use of that agent has been notified to the Executive in accordance with sub-paragraph (1), for any of the activities listed in paragraph 3(3) unless he has –

(a) notified the Executive in writing of his intention to do so at least 20 working days in advance, or such shorter period as the Executive may allow;

(b) furnished with that notification the particulars specified in sub-paragraph (5); and

(c) received the acknowledgement required by sub-paragraph (4).

(3) The Executive may accept a single notification under sub-paragraph (2) in respect of the use of more than one biological agent by the same person.

(4) Upon receipt of the notification required by sub-paragraph (1) or (2), the Executive shall, within 20 working days –

Schedule 3

(a) send to the notifier an acknowledgement of receipt; or
(b) if the notification does not contain all of the particulars specified in sub-paragraph (5) –
    (i) inform the notifier in writing of the further particulars required; and
    (ii) within 10 working days of receipt of those further particulars, send to the notifier an acknowledgement of receipt.

(5) The particulars to be included in the notification referred to in sub-paragraphs (1) and (2) shall be –

(a) the name and address of the employer and the address of the premises where the biological agent will be stored or used;
(b) the name, qualifications and relevant experience of any employee of that employer with specific responsibility for the health and safety of his fellow employees;
(c) the results of the risk assessment;
(d) the identity of the biological agent and, if the agent does not have an approved classification, the Group to which the agent has been assigned; and
(e) the preventive and protective measures that are to be taken.

(6) Where there are changes to processes, procedures or the biological agent which are of importance to health or safety at work and which render the original notification invalid the employer shall notify the Executive forthwith in writing of those changes.

(7) Sub-paragraphs (1) and (2) shall not apply in relation to a biological agent where an intention to use that biological agent has been previously notified to the Executive in accordance with the Genetically Modified Organisms (Contained Use) Regulations 2000.

(8) The requirement in sub-paragraph (1) to notify first use of a biological agent in Group 2 or 3 shall not apply to an employer whose only use of that agent is in relation to the provision of a diagnostic service provided that use will not involve a process likely to propagate, concentrate or otherwise increase the risk of exposure to that agent.

(9) The requirement in sub-paragraph (2) to notify use of a biological agent specified in Part V of this Schedule shall not apply to an employer whose only use of that agent is in relation to the provision of a diagnostic service provided that use will not involve a process likely to propagate, concentrate or otherwise increase the risk of exposure to that agent.

6 Notification of the consignment of biological agents

(1) An employer shall not consign a Group 4 biological agent or anything containing, or suspected of containing, such an agent to any other premises, whether or not those premises are under his ownership or control, unless he has notified the Executive in writing of his intention to do so at least 30 days in advance or before such shorter time as the Executive may approve and with that notification has furnished the particulars specified in sub-paragraph (4).

(2) Sub-paragraph (1) shall not apply where –

(a) the biological agent or material containing or suspected of containing such an agent is being consigned solely for the purpose of diagnosis;
(b) material containing or suspected of containing the biological agent is being consigned solely for the purpose of disposal; or

Schedule 3

(c) the biological agent is or is suspected of being present in a human patient or animal which is being transported for the purpose of medical treatment.

(3) Where a Group 4 biological agent is imported into Great Britain, the consignee shall give the notice required by sub-paragraph (1).

(4) The particulars to be included in the notification referred to in sub-paragraph (1) shall be –

(a) the identity of the biological agent and the volume of the consignment;
(b) the name of the consignor;
(c) the address of the premises from which it will be transported;
(d) the name of the consignee;
(e) the address of the premises to which it shall be transported;
(f) the name of the transport operator responsible for the transportation;
(g) the name of any individual who will accompany the consignment;
(h) the method of transportation;
(i) the packaging and any containment precautions which will be taken;
(j) the route which will be taken; and
(k) the proposed date of transportation.

PART II Containment measures for health and veterinary care facilities, laboratories and animal rooms

	Containment measures	Containment levels		
		2	3	4
1	The workplace is to be separated from any other activities in the same building.	No	Yes	Yes
2	Input air and extract air to the workplace are to be filtered using HEPA or equivalent.	No	Yes, on extract air	Yes, on input and double on extract air
3	Access is to be restricted to authorised persons only.	Yes	Yes	Yes, via air-lock key procedure
4	The workplace is to be sealable to permit disinfection.	No	Yes	Yes
5	Specified disinfection procedure.	Yes	Yes	Yes
6	The workplace is to be maintained at an air pressure negative to atmosphere.	No	Yes	Yes

Schedule 3		Containment measures	Containment levels		
			2	3	4
	7	Efficient vector control, eg rodents and insects.	Yes, for animal containment	Yes, for animal containment	Yes
	8	Surfaces impervious to water and easy to clean.	Yes, for bench	Yes, for bench and floor (and walls for animal containment)	Yes, for bench, floor, walls and ceiling
	9	Surfaces resistant to acids, alkalis, solvents, disinfectants.	Yes, for bench	Yes, for bench and floor (and walls for animal containment)	Yes, for bench, floor, walls and ceiling
	10	Safe storage of biological agents.	Yes	Yes	Yes, secure storage
	11	An observation window, or alternative, is to be present, so that occupants can be seen.	No	Yes	Yes
	12	A laboratory is to contain its own equipment.	No	Yes, so far as is reasonably practicable	Yes
	13	Infected material, including any animal, is to be handled in a safety cabinet or isolator or other suitable containment.	Yes, where aerosol produced	Yes, where aerosol produced	Yes
	14	Incinerator for disposal of animal carcases.	Accessible	Accessible	Yes, on site

Schedule	3

PART III Containment measures for industrial processes

	Containment measures	Containment levels		
		2	*3*	*4*
1	Viable micro-organisms should be contained in a system which physically separates the process from the environment (closed system).	Yes	Yes	Yes
2	Exhaust gases from the closed system should be treated so as to –	Minimise release	Prevent release	Prevent release
3	Sample collection, addition of materials to a closed system and transfer of viable micro-organisms to another closed system, should be performed so as to –	Minimise release	Prevent release	Prevent release
4	Bulk culture fluids should not be removed from the closed system unless the viable micro-organisms have been –	Inactivated by validated means	Inactivated by validated chemical or physical means	Inactivated by validated chemical or physical means
5	Seals should be designed so as to –	Minimise release	Prevent release	Prevent release
6	Closed systems should be located within a controlled area –	Optional	Optional	Yes, and purpose-built
	(a) biohazard signs should be posted;	Optional	Yes	Yes
	(b) access should be restricted to nominated personnel only;	Optional	Yes	Yes, via airlock
	(c) personnel should wear protective clothing;	Yes, work clothing	Yes	Yes, a complete change
	(d) decontamination and washing facilities should be provided for personnel;	Yes	Yes	Yes
	(e) personnel should shower before leaving the controlled area;	No	Optional	Yes

Schedule 3

	Containment measures	Containment levels		
		2	3	4
(f)	effluent from sinks and showers should be collected and inactivated before release;	No	Optional	Yes
(g)	the controlled area should be adequately ventilated to minimise air contamination;	Optional	Optional	Yes
(h)	the controlled area should be maintained at an air pressure negative to atmosphere;	No	Optional	Yes
(i)	input and extract air to the controlled area should be HEPA filtered;	No	Optional	Yes
(j)	the controlled area should be designed to contain spillage of the entire contents of closed system;	Optional	Yes	Yes
(k)	the controlled area should be sealable to permit fumigation.	No	Optional	Yes
7	Effluent treatment before final discharge.	Inactivated by validated means	Inactivated by validated chemical or physical means	Inactivated by validated physical means

PART IV Biohazard sign

The biohazard sign required by regulation 7(6)(a) shall be in the form shown below –

Schedule	3

PART V Biological agents whose use is to be notified in accordance with paragraph 5(2) of Part I of this Schedule

Any Group 3 or 4 agent.

The following Group 2 agents:

> *Bordetella pertussis*

> *Corynebacterium diphtheriae*

> *Neisseria meningitidis*

Schedule 4 Frequency of thorough examination and test of local exhaust ventilation plant used in certain processes

Schedule 4	*Regulation 9(2)(a)*

Column 1	Column 2
Process	**Minimum frequency**
Processes in which blasting is carried out in or incidental to the cleaning of metal castings, in connection with their manufacture.	1 month
Processes, other than wet processes, in which metal articles (other than of gold, platinum or iridium) are ground, abraded or polished using mechanical power, in any room for more than 12 hours in any week.	6 months
Processes giving off dust or fume in which non-ferrous metal castings are produced.	6 months
Jute cloth manufacture.	1 month

Schedule 5 Specific substances and processes for which monitoring is required

Schedule 5

Regulation 10(4)

Column 1	Column 2
Substance or process	**Minimum frequency**
Vinyl chloride monomer.	Continuous or in accordance with the Health and Safety Executive.[a]
Spray given off from vessels at which an electrolytic chromium process is carried on, except trivalent chromium.	Every 14 days while the process is being carried on.

(a)   Words substituted subject to transitional provisions as specified by SI 2008/960 Schedule 2, paragraph 11 the Legislative Reform (Health and Safety Executive) Order.

Schedule 6 Medical surveillance

Schedule 6	Regulation 11(2)(a) and (5)

Column 1	Column 2
Substances for which medical surveillance is appropriate	Process
Vinyl chloride monomer (VCM).	In manufacture, production, reclamation, storage, discharge, transport, use or polymerisation.
Nitro or amino derivatives of phenol and of benzene or its homologues.	In the manufacture of nitro or amino derivatives of phenol and of benzene or its homologues and the making of explosives with the use of any of these substances.
Potassium or sodium chromate or dichromate.	In manufacture.
Ortho-tolidine and its salts. Dianisidine and its salts. Dichlorobenzidine and its salts.	In manufacture, formation or use of these substances.
Auramine. Magenta.	In manufacture.
Carbon disulphide. Disulphur dichloride. Benzene, including benzol. Carbon tetrachloride. Trichlorethylene.	Processes in which these substances are used, or given off as vapour, in the manufacture of indiarubber or of articles or goods made wholly or partially of indiarubber.
Pitch.	In manufacture of blocks of fuel consisting of coal, coal dust, coke or slurry with pitch as a binding substance.

Schedule 7 Legislation concerned with the labelling of containers and pipes

Schedule	7

Regulation 12(5)
The Health and Safety (Safety Signs and Signals) Regulations 1996 (SI 1996/341);

The Good Laboratory Practice Regulations 1999 (SI 1999/3106);

[Words repealed by the Carriage of Dangerous Goods and Use of Transportable Pressure Equipment Regulations 2007/1573 Schedule 8, paragraph 1 (July 1, 2007)]

The Chemicals (Hazard Information and Packaging for Supply) Regulations 2002 (SI 2002/1689); and

The Carriage of Dangerous Goods and Use of Transportable Pressure Equipment Regulations 2007 (SI 2007/1573).[a]

(a)   *Words substituted by the Carriage of Dangerous Goods and Use of Transportable Pressure Equipment Regulations 2007/1573 Schedule, paragraph 1 (July 1, 2007).*

Schedule 8 Fumigations excepted from regulation 14

Schedule	8

Regulation 14(1)

Column 1	Column 2
Fumigant	**Nature of fumigation**
Hydrogen cyanide.	Fumigations carried out for research.
	Fumigations in fumigation chambers.
	Fumigations in the open air to control or kill mammal pests.
Methyl bromide.	Fumigations carried out for research.
	Fumigations in fumigation chambers.
	Fumigations of soil outdoors under gas-proof sheeting where not more than 1000 kg is used in any period of 24 hours on the premises.
	Fumigations of soil under gas-proof sheeting in glasshouses where not more than 500 kg is used in any period of 24 hours on the premises.
	Fumigations of compost outdoors under gas-proof sheeting where not more than 10 kg of methyl bromide is used in any period of 24 hours on the premises.
	Fumigations under gas-proof sheeting inside structures other than glasshouses and mushroom houses where not more than 5 kg of methyl bromide is used in each structure during any period of 24 hours.
	Fumigations of soil or compost in mushroom houses where not more than 5 kg of methyl bromide is used in any one fumigation in any period of 24 hours.
	Fumigations of containers where not more than 5 kg of methyl bromide is used in any one fumigation in a period of 24 hours.

			Column 1	Column 2
Schedule		**8**	*Fumigant*	*Nature of fumigation*
			Phosphine.	Fumigations carried out for research.
				Fumigations in fumigation chambers.
				Fumigations under gas-proof sheeting inside structures where not more than 1 kg of phosphine in each structure is used in any period of 24 hours.
				Fumigations in containers where not more than 0.5 kg of phosphine is used in any one fumigation in any period of 24 hours.
				Fumigations in individual impermeable packages.
				Fumigations in the open air to control or kill mammal pests.

Schedule 9 Notification of certain fumigations

| **Schedule** | **9** |

Regulation 14(2)

PART I Persons to whom notifications must be made

(1)   In the case of a fumigation to be carried out within the area of a harbour authority, advance notification of fumigation shall, for the purposes of regulation 14(2)(a), be given to –

(a)   *that authority;*
(b)   *an inspector appointed under section 19 of the 1974 Act, if that inspector so requires; and*
(c)   *where the fumigation –*
    (i)   *is to be carried out on a sea-going ship, the chief fire officer of the area in which the ship is situated and the officer in charge of the office of Her Majesty's Customs and Excise at the harbour; or*
    (ii)   *is the space fumigation of a building, the chief fire officer of the area in which the building is situated.*

(2)   In the case of a fumigation, other than a fumigation to which paragraph (1) applies, advance notification of fumigation shall be given to –

(a)   *the police officer for the time being in charge of the police station for the police district in which the fumigation is carried out;*
(b)   *an inspector appointed under section 19 of the 1974 Act, if that inspector so requires; and*
(c)   *where the fumigation is to be carried out on a sea-going ship or is the space fumigation of a building, the chief fire officer of the area in which the ship or building is situated.*

PART II Information to be given in advance notice of fumigations

(3)   The information to be given in a notification made for the purposes of regulation 14(2) shall include the following –

(a)   *the name, address and place of business of the fumigator and his telephone number;*
(b)   *the name of the person requiring the fumigation to be carried out;*
(c)   *the address and description of the premises where the fumigation is to be carried out;*

Schedule 9

(d)   the date on which the fumigation is to be carried out and the estimated time of commencement and completion;

(e)   the name of the operator in charge of the fumigation; and

(f)   the fumigant to be used.

Appendix 1 Notice of Approval

By virtue of section 16(4) of the Health and Safety at Work etc Act 1974, and with the consent of the Secretary of State for Work and Pensions, the Health and Safety Executive has on 30 October 2013 approved the revised Code of Practice entitled *Control of substances hazardous to health* (Sixth edition, 2013, L5).

The revised Code of Practice gives practical guidance on the Control of Substances Hazardous to Health Regulations 2002 (as amended).

By virtue of section 16(5), and with the consent of the Secretary of State for Work and Pensions under that paragraph, the Health and Safety Executive has withdrawn its approval of the Code of Practice entitled *Control of substances hazardous to health* (Fifth edition), which came into effect on 6 April 2005 and which shall cease to have effect on 2 December 2013.

The Code of Practice comes into effect on 2 December 2013.

Signed

SUE JOHNS
Secretary to the Board of the Health and Safety Executive

14 November 2013

References

1   BS EN 481:1993 *Workplace atmospheres. Size fraction definitions for measurement of airborne particles* British Standards Institution

2   *Legionnaires' disease: The control of legionella bacteria in water systems. Approved Code of Practice and guidance on regulations* L8 (Fourth edition) HSE Books 2013 ISBN 978 0 7176 6615 7 www.hse.gov.uk/pubns/books/L8.htm

3   *The Approved List of biological agents* MISC208(rev2) HSE 2013 www.hse.gov.uk/pubns/misc208.htm

4   *EH40/2005 Workplace exposure limits: Containing the list of workplace exposure limits for use with the Control of Substances Hazardous to Health Regulations (as amended)* Environmental Hygiene Guidance Note EH40 (Second edition) HSE Books 2011 ISBN 978 0 7176 6446 7 www.hse.gov.uk/pubns/books/EH40.htm

5   *Workplace health, safety and welfare. Workplace (Health, Safety and Welfare) Regulations 1992. Approved Code of Practice* L24 (Second edition) HSE Books 2013 ISBN 978 0 7176 6583 9 www.hse.gov.uk/pubns/books/L24.htm

6   *Health and Safety at Work etc Act 1974 (c.37)* The Stationery Office 1974 ISBN 978 0 10 543774 1

7   *Biological agents: Managing the risks in laboratories and healthcare premises* HSE 2005 www.hse.gov.uk/biosafety/biologagents.pdf

8   *Managing skin exposure risks at work* HSG262 HSE Books 2009 ISBN 978 0 7176 6309 5 www.hse.gov.uk/pubns/books/hsg262.htm

9   *Respiratory protective equipment at work: A practical guide* HSG53 (Fourth edition) HSE Books 2013 ISBN 978 0 7176 6454 2 www.hse.gov.uk/pubns/books/HSG53.htm

10   *Controlling airborne contaminants at work: A guide to local exhaust ventilation (LEV)* HSG258 (Second edition) HSE Books 2011 ISBN 978 0 7176 6415 3 www.hse.gov.uk/pubns/books/HSG258.htm

11   *Monitoring strategies for toxic substances* HSG173 (Second edition) HSE Books 2006 ISBN 978 0 7176 6188 6 www.hse.gov.uk/pubns/books/HSG173.htm

12   *Biological monitoring in the workplace: A guide to its practical application to chemical exposure* HSG167 (Second edition) HSE Books 1997 ISBN 978 0 7176 1279 6 www.hse.gov.uk/pubns/books/HSG167.htm

13   BS 1710:1984 *Specification for identification of pipelines and services* British Standards Institution

Further information

For information about health and safety visit https://books.hse.gov.uk or http://www.hse.gov.uk. You can view HSE guidance online and order priced publications from the website. HSE priced publications are also available from bookshops.

To report inconsistencies or inaccuracies in this guidance email: commissioning@wlt.com.

British Standards can be obtained in PDF or hard copy formats from BSI: http://shop.bsigroup.com or by contacting BSI Customer Services for hard copies only Tel: 0845 086 9001 email: cservices@bsigroup.com.

The Stationery Office publications are available from The Stationery Office, PO Box 29, Norwich NR3 1GN Tel: 0333 202 5070 Fax: 0333 202 5080 email: customer.services@tso.co.uk Website: www.tsoshop.co.uk/ (They are also available from bookshops.) Statutory Instruments can be viewed free of charge at www.legislation.gov.uk/, where you can also search for changes to legislation.